D0421801

geometry

the size and shape of everyday math

geometry

the size and shape of everyday math

mike askew

and sheila ebbutt

METRO BOOKS
NEW YORK

This 2011 edition published by Metro Books,
by arrangement with Quid Publishing

Conceived, designed and produced by
Quid Publishing
Level 4 Sheridan House
114 Western Road
England
Hove BN3 1DD

Design by Lindsey Johns

Image on page 56 © Dreamstime; image on page 65 © Dreamstime; image on page 119 © Margaret Wetheim; image on page 140 © Kmhkmh | Creative Commons; image on page 162 © George M. Bergman; image on page 170 © Rama | Creative Commons

Metro Books
122 Fifth Avenue
New York, NY 10011

ISBN: 978-1-4351-2758-6

Printed and bound in China

1 3 5 7 9 10 8 6 4 2

CONTENTS

GEOMETRY: AN INTRODUCTION

There are two sides to the coin of mathematics: discrete and continuous mathematics. Discrete mathematics deals with quantities that can be counted—sheep, football crowds, bottles. The earliest evidence of humankind dealing with discrete quantities is the Ishango bone, which has tally marks grouped in such a way that they appear to have been used for calculations of some sort. Not all phenomena can be counted, however. Clay, beer, land, and the like are continuous quantities that have to be measured. Measuring is a way of making the uncountable countable, and the roots of geometry are embedded in measurement.

While early civilizations undoubtedly found ways to deal and trade with continuous quantities such as olive oil or wine, the origins of the word "geometry" lie with the farmers of the Nile Delta. The annual flooding of the Nile Delta washed away the records of who owned which pieces of land. Ways had to be devised to accurately mark out plots, and geometry—literally meaning "earth measure" in Greek—developed.

Father of Geometry

Asked to name famous Greek mathematicians, many people would come up with Pythagoras and possibly Euclid. Although not fashionable in school now, "Euclid's elements" would probably have rung bells with our grandparents, and Euclid is often referred to as the father of geometry. In fairness, that title more befits Thales of Ionia (640–546 BCE), who made a study of geometry some 300 years before Euclid. Although there are no writings passed down from Thales, there are many stories about him, a famous one being that he found a method for calculating the height of the Great Pyramid of Cheops, built around 2600 BCE. It is not known specifically what elements of geometry were used by the Egyptians in the design and construction of the pyramids, but it seems that figuring out the overall height had been a long-standing puzzle. Thales' insight was to notice that, at a certain time, his shadow was as long as he was tall. Waiting until the Sun was positioned in the sky such that his own shadow equaled his height, he measured the length of the pyramid's shadow from its base. Adding half the length of the base of the pyramid to the length of the shadow, Thales reasoned, would give the height of the pyramid.

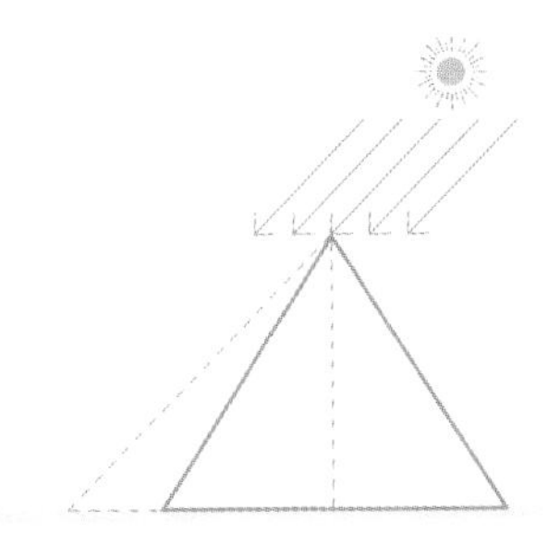

• With the Sun in the right position, Thales was able to use the lengths of shadows to find the height of the Pyramids.

Thales is also credited with insights such as the fact that a diameter of a circle always cuts the circle exactly in half, or the observation that in an isosceles triangle (a triangle with two equal sides) the angles opposite the equal sides are also equal. Today, even a self-confessed math-phobic would probably not be too surprised by these "insights," regarding them as common sense rather than deeply mathematical. But to the thinkers of Thales' day, such observations were major steps forward in mathematics in that Thales was drawing conclusions about all circles, or all isosceles triangles. This deductive mindset was a new way of thinking about mathematics, moving away from mathematics being a purely practical enterprise that dealt with particular circles or triangles to the abstract study of generalities. Thales set in motion the style of thinking from which modern mathematics has grown.

Thales thus shifted attention from the measurement aspect of geometry to the study of invariants: properties of circles or isosceles triangles that remain constant irrespective of size. The diameters of circles change, but they all remain invariant in bisecting the circle. If one thing can be regarded as linking the disparate branches of geometry, it is the study of invariance.

Heart of Geometry: Invariance and Symmetry

When people talk about symmetry, they are usually using it in the everyday, informal sense of images that are pleasingly balanced. The symmetry of a butterfly's wings, the five-point petal design you get when you slice an apple in half, a beautiful smiling portrait.

These informal, almost intuitive senses of symmetry are more formally developed in Euclidean geometry as the study of reflective and rotational symmetry. The butterfly has reflective symmetry in the same way that the word "MUM" has reflective symmetry (hold it up and it reads the same in a mirror, or align a mirror vertically through the "U" and it still reads the same). Incidentally, psychologists have established that we

• The natural world is full of examples of reflective symmetry, from leaves and snowflakes to the markings on a butterfly's wings.

are more drawn to human faces that are not perfectly symmetrical than to those that are, which is just as well since most faces are less than symmetrical.

The petal design at the center of an apple has mirror symmetry, but it also has rotational symmetry: a "perfect" five-petal flower can be rotated (through 72°) into five positions and still look the same after each rotation.

One of the things that drives mathematicians is the desire to extend ideas and apply them to new contexts. So the everyday sense of symmetry through reflection and rotation is extended to a mathematical meaning, which defines a mathematical object as symmetric with respect to a particular mathematical operation if that operation, when applied to the object, preserves some property of the object.

Wait, don't stop reading, here is what that means in plain English: the term "mathematical object" is used to distinguish between "real-world" objects and the ideal (in the sense of perfect) "mathematical" object. In the real world, an actual butterfly is never going to be perfectly symmetrical: very close examination will reveal slight mismatches in the two wings. Even a very carefully drawn picture of a symmetrical butterfly, if enlarged to a huge scale, will reveal some minute mismatches. To all intents and purposes in our daily lives, such imperfections are likely not to be noticeable or important, but they matter to the mathematician who thrives on absolute perfection. As we shall see later, one of the lasting legacies of Euclid was to make this distinction between the real and the ideal. Geometry deals with mathematical objects such as points, lines, polygons, polyhedra, and, unrecognizable to Euclid, fractals.

In the case of our (mathematical) butterfly, the mathematical operation applied is reflection; it preserves the look of the butterfly to the extent that it is impossible to decide if you are looking at the original butterfly or at its reflection. Similarly, applying the operation of rotation to the apple core preserves the look of it.

We are now in a position to extend the meaning of symmetry. Consider taking a triangle and uniformly expanding it (scaling it up) or contracting it (scaling it down). In everyday parlance we would not talk of these different versions of the triangle as being symmetrical. But the mathematical operation of scaling (up or down) preserves

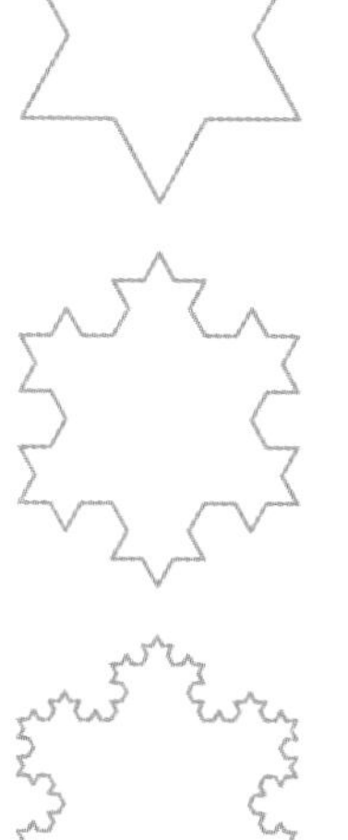

• The Koch snowflake is a uniquely difficult problem in geometry, as its area cannot be stated with 100% accuracy (see pp. 166–167).

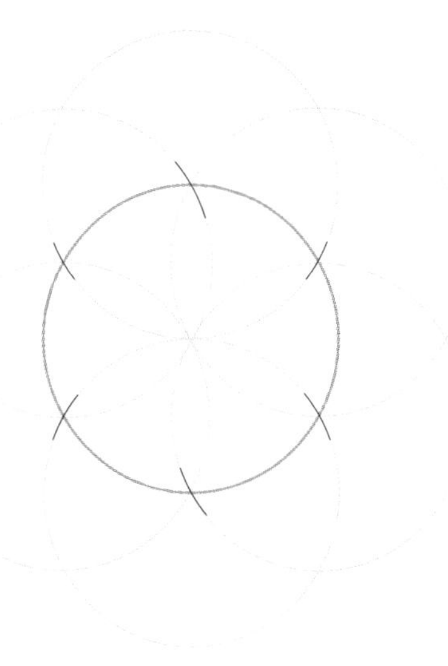

• Using basic mathematical tools such as a straight edge and compasses, it is possible to construct multi-sided polygons (see pp. 20–21).

certain properties of the triangle; for example, the sizes of the angles do not change and the relative proportions of the sides are invariant. Triangles are symmetric with respect to scaling in terms of properties of angle and ratios of sides. Creating an image of a triangle by moving it about the plane, without rotating it—known as the mathematical operation of "translation"—now also gets counted as a symmetry, as the properties of the triangle are preserved as it is moved around.

These basic symmetries—reflection, rotation, scaling, translation—and combinations of them, provide the basis of the study of Euclidean geometry; that is, the geometry of plane figures. Plane figures are those that can be represented in perfectly flat two dimensions (and extended into three dimensions through vertical planes). The study of these symmetries is the geometry that is familiar to most of us through school. The "facts" that are taught—for example, that the angles of a triangle always add up to 180°—are all rooted in these symmetries. They can also be used to deduce less commonly known facts, such as that there are essentially only 14 different types of wallpaper patterns.

SYMMETRY IN STATISTICS

The familiar bell-shaped curve represents a class of statistical distributions that are known as "normal" distributions. Although based on a mathematical equation, the idea of "normal" is based on the range of measurements that occur in nature—for example, the range of heights of adults in a population roughly fits the bell-shaped curve. The symmetrical nature of the curve is used to shape things such as tests of mathematics. If the shape of the curve is not symmetrical but skewed in one direction or the other, a test may need to be adjusted to make it easier or harder.

Non-Euclidean Geometry

As it became clear that Earth was not flat but actually a sphere, some of the Euclidean "facts" that had become almost self-evidently true were challenged. For example, boats could travel in straight lines, make three turns, and end up back where they started, traversing the three sides of a triangle. As methods of measuring and calculating improved, it became clear that the angles that the boat turned through—a triangle on a sphere—added up to more than 180°. Thus was opened up the possibility of new geometries—the non-Euclidean geometries.

The symmetries of the non-Euclidean geometries also specify what remains invariant under mathematical operations. Projective geometry looks at what stays the same when geometrical objects in one context are represented in another form; for example, when a three dimensional object is projected onto a two-dimensional plane, or when figures on a sphere are projected onto a two-dimensional plane. As Italian Renaissance artists understood to their benefit, in projective geometry, parallel lines do meet.

The geometry of topology examines the symmetries of more extreme transformations. Often referred to as "rubber sheet" geometry, topology is the study of how shapes can be transformed into other shapes as though they were made of flexible rubber. Imagine, for example, an inflated rubber ring like a hollow donut. This can, in theory, be stretched and transformed into some-

• The development of projective geometry introduced the use of "vanishing points" in paintings, giving them a more "realistic" perspective.

thing resembling a teacup. But it cannot, without tearing and repairing the rubber surface, be transformed into a hollow sphere. In the geometry of topology, donuts , and cups are symmetrical!

Scale symmetry is one of the cornerstones of Euclidean geometry—if triangles and circles did not have the same properties when enlarged or reduced in size, much of Euclidean geometry would not hold true. In the real world, however, such scale symmetry is rare. For example, ants or spiders, if scaled up to be the monsters of some sci-fi films, could not survive (the ratio of body volume to body surface area necessitates the development of lungs in larger creatures). The legs of an elephant are not simply a larger version of the legs of a mouse.

The lack of application of Euclidean geometry to the real world led to the development of the geometry of fractals, which encompasses naturally occurring phenomena that do have a form of scale symmetry. Fractals are mathematical objects with the key feature of being "self-similar," in that they look the same irrespective of the level of magnification. This is a different form of scale symmetry from the Euclidean—enlarging part of a triangle will not look like a triangle. The Mandelbrot set fractal is the most famous mathematical fractal.

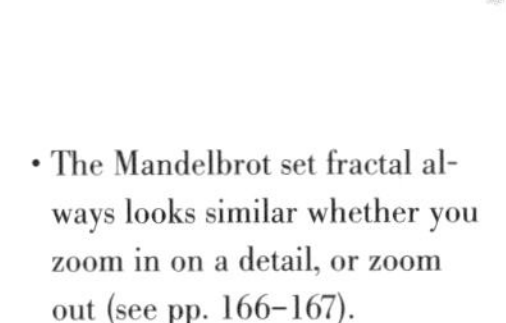

• The Mandelbrot set fractal always looks similar whether you zoom in on a detail, or zoom out (see pp. 166–167).

Fractal similarity is common in nature. Coastlines have a fractal structure since they appear to have roughly the same outline whether viewed from the air or under a microscope. Trees, ferns , and broccoli all display similar properties.

The mathematician Johannes Kepler described geometry as having two jewels: the theorem of Pythagoras and the golden ratio. We explore these jewels in the following chapters, but since Kepler's day the new geometries, including topology and fractals, have revealed many more jewels, which we also share with you here.

"The most complex object in mathematics, the Mandelbrot set . . . is so complex as to be uncontrollable by mankind and describable as 'chaos.' "

—Benoît Mandelbrot

Chapter

1

Points, Lines, and Circles

When you sing, as Julie Andrews reminds us, you begin with *doh*, *ray*, *me*. Geometry is generally seen as beginning with points, lines, and circles and, just as symphonies can be constructed out of a few notes, mathematicians were able to construct a wide range of geometrical objects from these few favorite things.

CONSTRUCTIONS I

Where does geometry exist? Do squares exist in the real world or only in the ideal world of mathematics? Euclid suggested that in geometry, drawings could only illustrate ideas; drawings are not the ideas themselves. Geometry, according to Euclid, only exists in the realm of the imagination.

Ideal Mathematical Objects

Although best known for his "postulates," Euclid caused something of a stir in mathematics with his definitions. He defined a point as "that which has no part" and a line as "breadthless length"; in doing so he made the distinction between the mathematical "ideal" (which only exists in the imagination) and the real. If we argue that a point exists, then we must also conclude that it can be divided up into smaller parts. But if a point "has no part" then it cannot be divided up. Ergo, it cannot actually exist in the material world. Similarly, if a line is "breadthless" it cannot exist. So the whole of geometry as we popularly know it is based on things that don't actually exist; it's a paradox.

What do exist are representations of these ideal mathematical objects, and the Ancient Greeks were fascinated by the construction of geometrical representations. These days there are a vast number of tools available to use for geometrical constructions, ranging from the humble protractor to computer-assisted design. The Greeks, however, relied somewhat parsimoniously on:

- a straight edge to draw straight lines (not a measuring rule—no units, just lines); and

- a pair of compasses for drawing circles.

With just these bare essentials, the Greek geometers were able to construct a wide range of representations and solve many geometrical problems. As we are going to need some of these constructions on our journey, here's a reminder of some you might have met at school.

Constructing a Perpendicular Bisector of a Line Segment

This two-for-the-price-of-one construction is used to produce right angles and/or cut a line segment into two equal parts.

The straight edge is used to draw a line segment of whatever length. Let's label one end A and the other B. The compasses are set to any length greater than half of the length AB. With the compass point on A, draw an arc above the line and a similar one below it. Keeping the compasses set to the same distance, draw two similar arcs with the point on B. Using the straight edge to join the points where each pair of arcs intersect constructs a line that is perpendicular (at right angles) to and that bisects the length of the line AB.

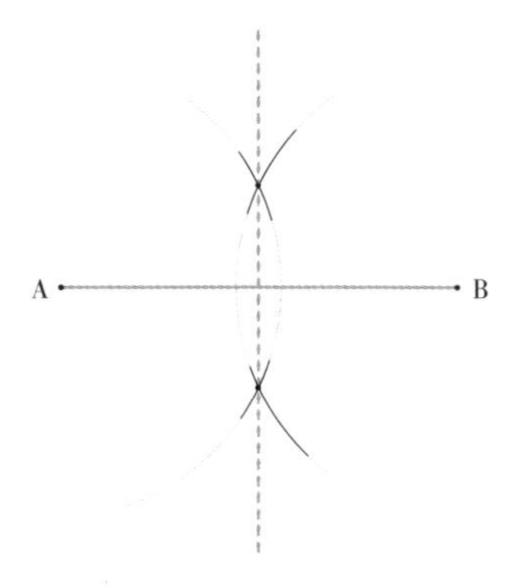

Bisecting an Angle

The straight edge is used to draw two line segments that meet to create an angle (O). Set the compasses to any length and, with the compass point on O, draw an arc that crosses each arm of the angle, at points M and N, say. Move the compass point to M and draw an arc between the two straight lines. Keeping the compasses set to the same distance, draw an arc from point N to intersect the arc from M. Use the straight edge to join O to this point of intersection P. The line OP bisects the angle O.

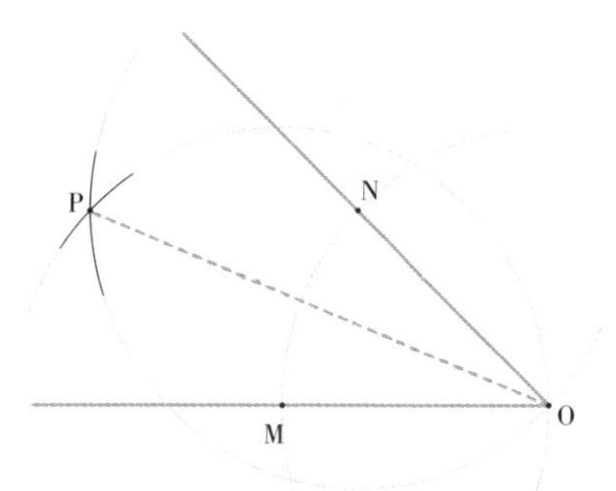

The mathematically astute reader will note that we've made some claims here that look reasonable but have not actually been proved. It certainly looks like OP bisects the angle, but how do we know for certain that it does? Congruent triangles (see pp. 44–45) help us establish the truth of our claim deductively. Joining M and N each to P creates two triangles, OMP and ONP.

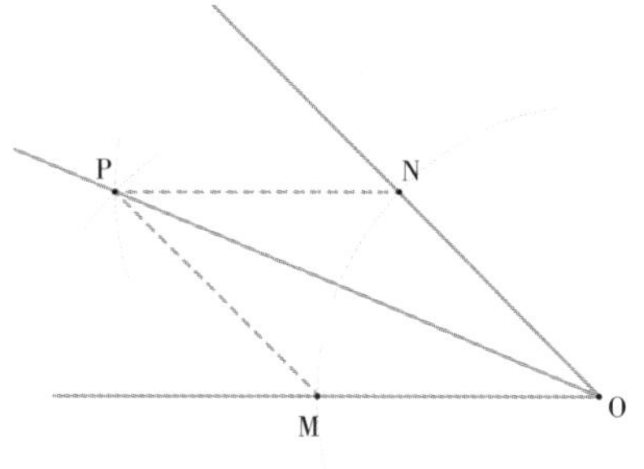

Because of the way we constructed the lines, MO = NO and, similarly, MP = NP. OP is a line common to both triangles, so ΔOMP and ΔONP are congruent (SSS). Hence $\angle$MOP = $\angle$NOP. A similar logic can be used to establish the veracity of the perpendicular bisector construction.

More Parsimony

The Danish mathematician Georg Mohr proposed that it was only the compasses that were doing all the work here. In 1672 he demonstrated that although you need the straight edge to join various points together, only the compasses are really essential. Lorenzo Mascheroni confirmed this over 100 years later, gilding his proofs by writing them in verse.

CONSTRUCTIONS 2

With their basic tools of straight edge and compasses, followers of Euclid were equipped to construct a variety of polygons, starting with the humble but important equilateral triangle.

Constructing an Equilateral Triangle

We are only interested in the shape, not size, of our triangle, so a length of any measurement provides the base of the triangle.

We put the compass point on A, set the radius to be the length AB and draw an arc.

Keeping the radius fixed at that size, move the compass point to B, and draw an arc from A that crosses the first arc at C.

Joining AC and BC completes the triangle.

How can we be certain that the sides are all the same length? Well, AC is the same length as AB as they are both radii of a circle; similarly, BC must be the same length as AB. So AB = AC = BC and our triangle is equilateral. Although fairly obvious, this little "proof" is typical of Euclidean geometry in that results are established through logical reasoning rather than measurement. The logic must hold for all sizes of triangle and is more convincing than doing the

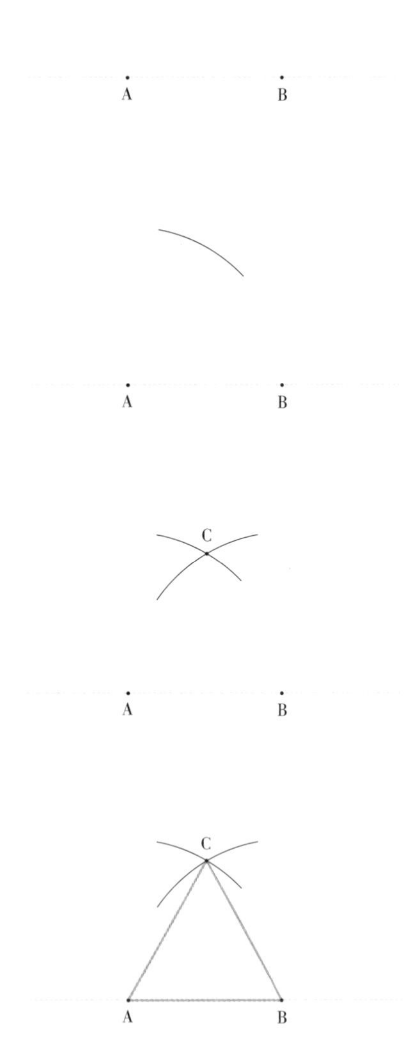

actual measuring, of which, the skeptical mathematician would say, "Well, it may hold for that particular case, but how can you know it will be true of any size of triangle?"

Constructing a Square

We saw earlier how to construct a line perpendicular to another, that is at right angles (pp. 14–15).

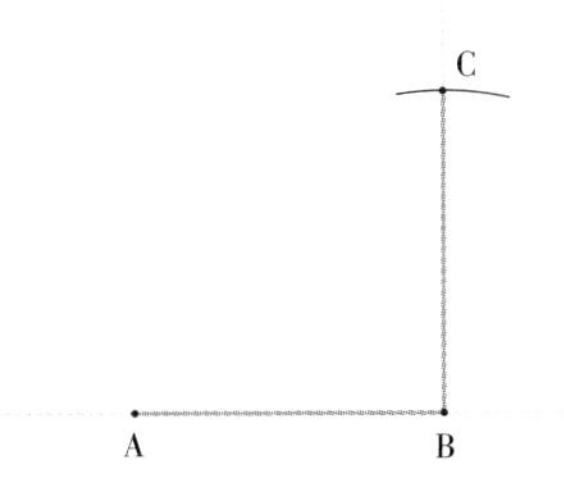

The length of the sides of our square is going to be AB. So with the compass point on B and the pencil on A, draw the arc that crosses the vertical line at C.

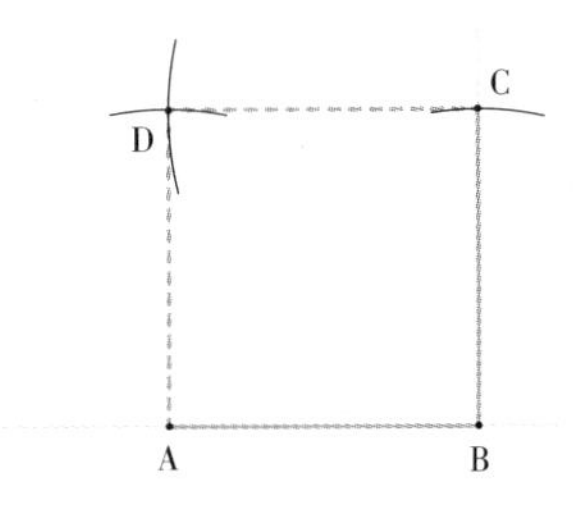

Keeping the compasses set to that distance, we put the point on A and draw an arc, then on C, marking the point of intersection as D. Joining AD and CD completes the square. Applying similar logic to that which we used with the equilateral triangle, we can establish that all the sides must be the same length and all the angles right angles.

CONSTRUCTING THE PENTAGON

The equilateral triangle and the square were easy to construct, so we might expect that constructing a regular pentagon should be easy.

In fact, as we shall see, the pentagon proves to be not at all easy and stumped mathematicians for quite some time.

Profile

Euclid

Euclid is known as the father of geometry. Nine of "the elements" are about plane and solid geometry; the other four are about number theory. The style of the books varies and Euclid probably worked with a group of mathematicians who all contributed. Each book contains a number of definitions followed by theorems. You may be familiar with such theorems in geometry from school—those proofs that end in "QED."

Until the 19th century, Euclid's system of plane geometry as set out in *The Elements* was considered the only geometry. Then, when mathematicians started work on other kinds of geometry, based on curved surfaces, the terms Euclidean geometry and non-Euclidean geometry were formed to distinguish the two kinds.

The Life of Euclid

Euclid was born around 360 BCE and died in about 230 BCE. Very little is known about his life. During the reign of Ptolemy the First, Euclid taught mathematics in Alexandria, in Egypt, where he had been a pupil of the followers of Plato, and where Pythagoras had studied. He was an influence on Archimedes and Eratosthenes, who studied in Alexandria after Euclid. His significant work, *The Elements*, is based on the works of mathematicians and philosophers he studied, such as Plato, Aristotle, Eudoxus, Thales, Hippocrates, and Pythagoras. It is said that when Ptolemy was presented with the 13 books of *The Elements*, he asked if there were a shorter way to learn geometry, and Euclid answered, "There is no royal road to geometry."

Euclid's Theorems

In Book I of *The Elements*, Euclid gave 22 definitions of the basic terms of geometry. The first four of these are:

- A point is that which has no part.
- A line is length without width.
- The ends of a line are points.
- A straight line is a line that lies evenly with the points on itself.

He then set out ten axioms as a basis for mathematics—axioms are statements that we accept as true.

• Euclid's works

Manuscript versions of The Elements *were available in Latin and Arabic, but it was not printed until the 15th century in Venice, and then in English in 1570. The publication of* The Elements *had a significant influence on the study of mathematics in Europe, and Euclid was taught in schools from the 18th century onward, not only for pupils to learn geometry, but also to learn logic.*

Apart from The Elements, *five other books of Euclid have survived. Each follows the same pattern of* The Elements, *with definitions, axioms, and theorems. There are works on geometric problems, ratio, the mathematics of mirrors, moving spheres, and perspective.*

But Euclid believed that axioms couldn't be taken as true without proof, so he devised logical steps to prove the axioms. Euclid divided his ten axioms into two groups of five. The first five are "common notions" general to mathematics. The remaining five he called "postulates," and these are specific to geometry:

- You can draw a straight line between any two points.
- You can extend the line indefinitely.
- You can draw a circle using any line segment as the radius and one end point as the center.
- All right angles are equal.
- Given a line and a point, you can draw only one line through the point that is parallel to the first line.

The geometric proofs in *The Elements* are based on construction—you need to draw the diagrams to prove the propositions, using only a straight edge and a pair of compasses. The straight edge has no measurement marks: the measurements can only be ratios produced by the compasses. Euclid builds up propositions, one leading to the next, starting from the construction of an equilateral triangle, and leading on to the next. This is a logical approach, called the axiomatic method.

Here is an example of one of Euclid's theorems, Proposition 6 in Book 1. This one proposes that, if two angles of a triangle are equal, then the sides opposite them will be equal. In this theorem Euclid uses proof by contradiction, also known as *reductio ad absurdum*, where you suppose an obviously true statement to be false, and this leads you to an absurd conclusion.

Theorem 6

Let ABC be a triangle in which angle ABC is equal to angle ACB; then side AB will equal side AC.

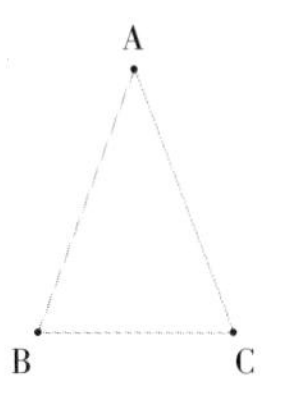

If AB is not equal to AC, then one of them is longer.

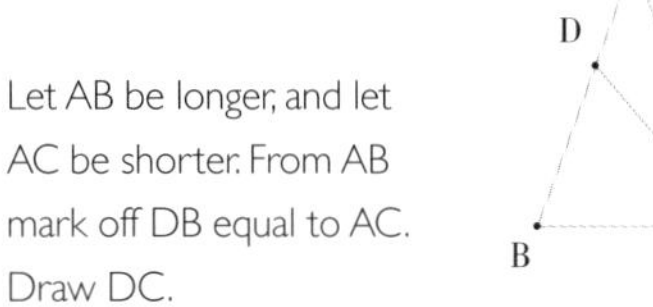

Let AB be longer, and let AC be shorter. From AB mark off DB equal to AC. Draw DC.

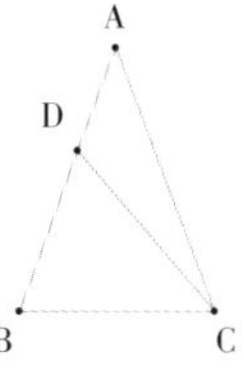

We have constructed DB equal to AC.

BC is common to triangles DBC and ACB
The two sides DB, BC are equal to the two sides AC, CB respectively.

The angle DBC is equal to angle ACB.
∴ triangles DBC, ACB are equal areas, the smaller to the larger—which is absurd.

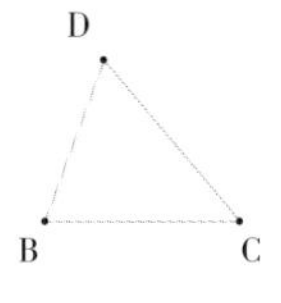

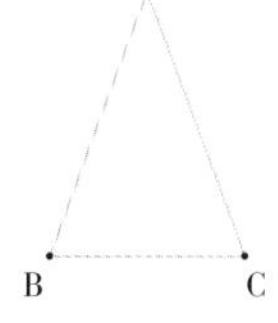

∴ the assumption that AB is not equal to AC is false; that is, it is equal to it.
∴ if two angles of a triangle are equal, then the sides opposite them will be equal.

Floral Clock

THE PROBLEM:

Felicity saw a floral clock in her local park and thought it would be nice to mark out the 12 points of the clock around the edge of a circular flowerbed. Using only a straight edge and compasses, how can she construct a 12-sided polygon (the dodecagon)?

THE METHOD:

We know how to construct an equilateral triangle and six such triangles will fit neatly together to form a hexagon.

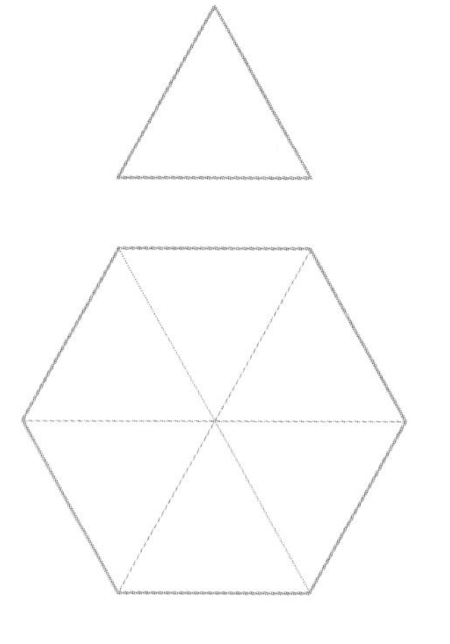

There is a way of constructing the hexagon without going to the bother of constructing the six triangles first. Recall how the equilateral triangle was constructed by setting the compasses to a fixed distance and using that to draw arcs to set the lengths of the sides (p. 16). So begin by drawing a circle. Keeping the compasses to the same distance, start with the point at any position on the circumference, and mark off an arc that intersects the circumference. Move the compass point to that intersection and mark off the next point round. Continuing in this way, you can mark six equally spaced points around the circumference.

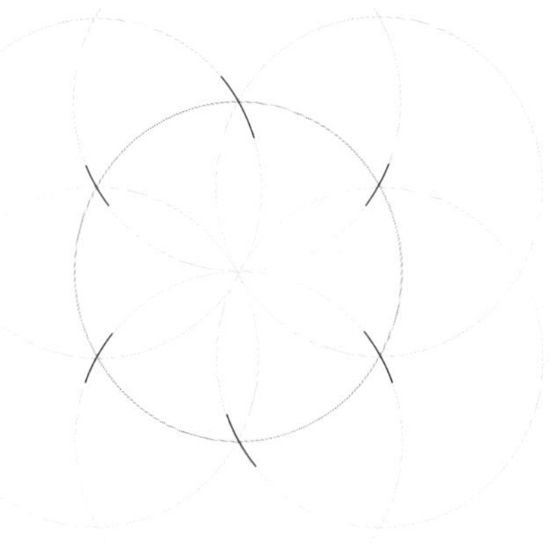

Join these six points up to create the hexagon.

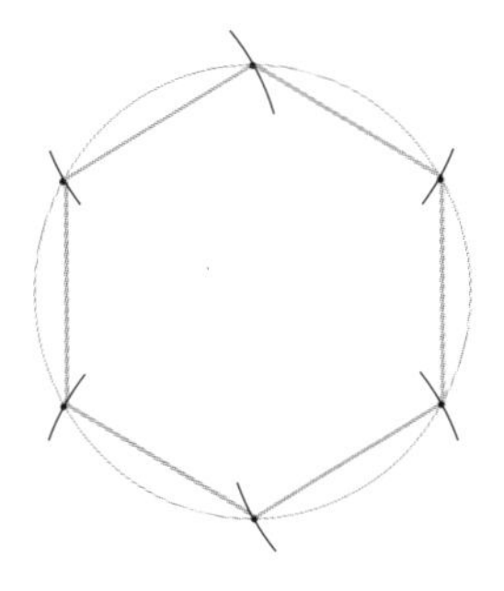

We saw earlier how to bisect a line with a perpendicular line. Felicity now bisects each side of the hexagon, extending the perpendicular line to cut the circumference of the circle.

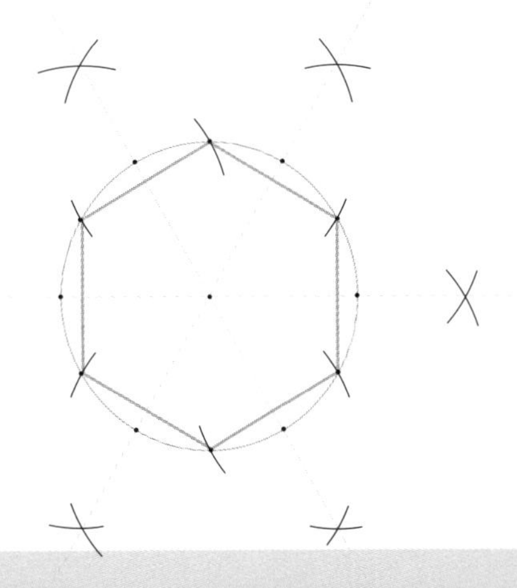

Joining up the 12 points around the circumference creates the dodecagon.

THE SOLUTION:

Felicity constructs the 12-sided shape by constructing the simpler hexagon. By bisecting the sides of the hexagon she creates 12 points around the circumference of the circle, which form the vertices of the dodecagon.

Exercise 2

Tabletop

THE PROBLEM:

Carpenter Rob has an order for a regular pentagonal tabletop. Using only his straight edge and compasses, how does Rob mark out the perfect pentagon? Can he easily extend the method for constructing a hexagon to this end?

THE METHOD:

Rob had made a hexagonal top by fitting six equilateral triangles together. He reasons that five isosceles triangles will fit together to make the pentagon.

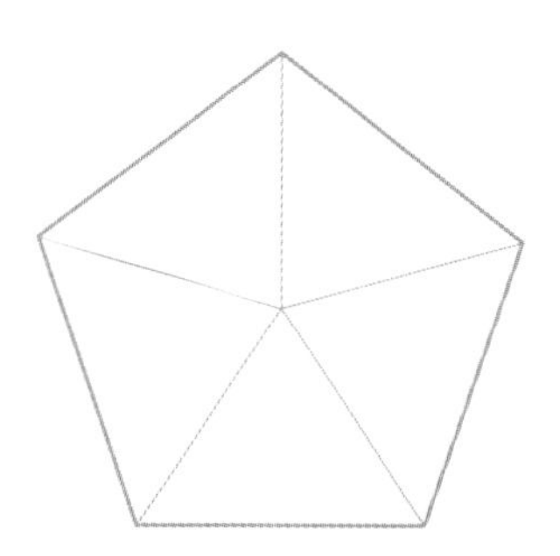

The five angles at the center of the pentagon must add up to 360°. So the angle at the vertex of each triangle is 72°. Not the easiest angle to construct with only a pair of compasses. Rob wondered whether a ten-sided shape (a decagon) would be easier to construct than a five-sided shape. If it were, he could make the pentagon by joining up every other vertex of the decagon. Ten isosceles triangles will fit together to make a decagon, so the vertex of each must be 36°. That leaves 180° – 36° = 144° for the other two angles, so each of these must be 72°. There's that pesky 72° again.

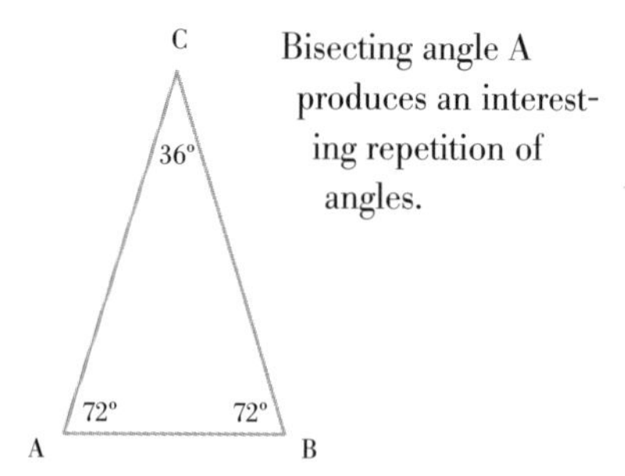

Bisecting angle A produces an interesting repetition of angles.

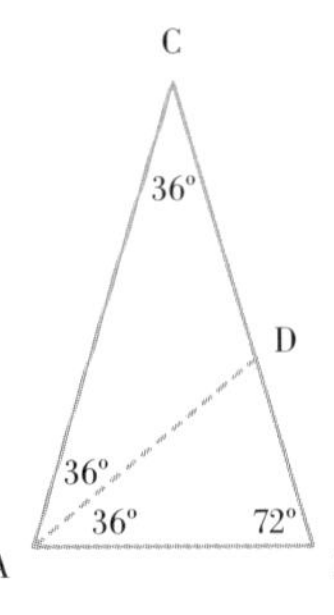

ΔACB is isosceles with 36° at the vertex, and two equal angles of 72°. ΔABD has an angle of 36° and one angle of 72°, so the other angle must be 180° – (36° + 72°) = 72°. This is another isosceles triangle and similar to ΔACB. If ΔACB and ΔABD are similar, then the ratio of their sides must be in proportion. We can set the length of sides AC (and BC) as 1 unit and AB as x. That makes AD also have length x and CD also x. So BD is $1 - x$ units long.

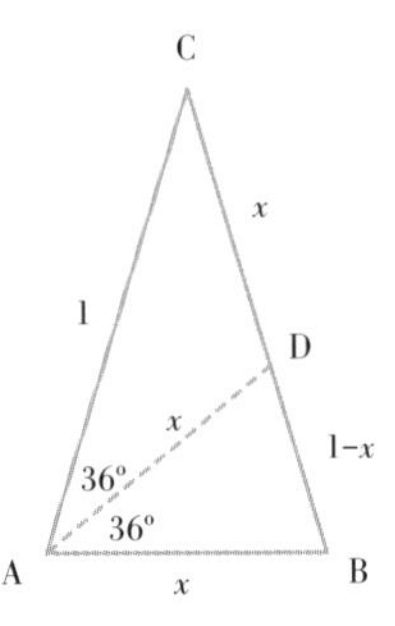

Comparing the ratio of the sides of ΔACB and ΔABD.

$$\frac{1}{x} = \frac{x}{(1 - x)}$$

This is related to the golden ratio (see pp. 64–65) and has the solution:

$$x = \frac{(1 + \sqrt{5})}{2}$$

Now we must construct the length $\sqrt{5}$. A spiral starting with a right-angled triangle produces $\sqrt{2}$; building on that leads to other square roots.

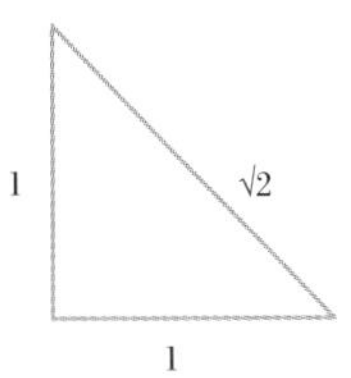

In the second triangle, using Pythagoras' theorem (see pp. 54–55):

$$x^2 = (\sqrt{2})^2 + 1^2 = 2 + 1$$

$$\text{So } x = \sqrt{3}$$

Continuing in this way leads to $\sqrt{5}$.

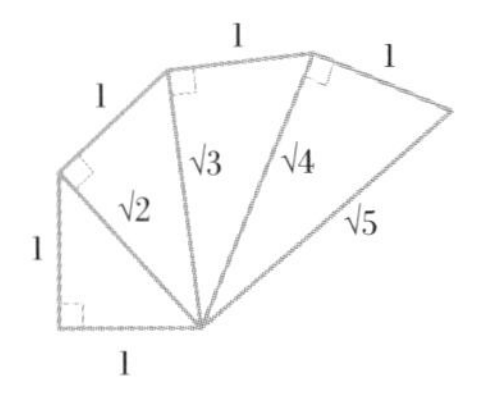

THE SOLUTION:

Rob uses his compasses to mark off a length of one unit, adds on the length of $\sqrt{5}$ and bisects the total length. This gives the base of his triangle. Setting his compasses to the unit length, he can construct the isosceles triangle of which ten fit together to create a decagon. Joining every other vertex creates the regular pentagon.

THE IMPOSSIBILITY OF SEVEN

Armed only with a pair of compasses and a straight edge, the early geometers could easily construct three-, four-, and six-sided polygons and, with a bit of ingenuity, a regular pentagon. By adapting these, were they able to construct any regular polygon they wished?

Taking Stock

By bisecting angles and lengths, Euclid showed how the number of sides of a polygon could continue to be doubled. The square forms the basis of the octagon, the octagon a 16-sided polygon, then a 32-gon, 64-gon and so on. These numbers are powers of two—that is, two multiplied by itself repeatedly. If we multiply two by itself five times, we call this two to the power of 5. So $2^5 = 2 \times 2 \times 2 \times 2 \times 2$. Because there are four sides to a square, the sides of a polygon that emerge from a square are all four times a power of 2, written as 4×2^n. For example, suppose $n = 7$, then $2^7 = 128$, and $4 \times 128 = 512$. We can construct a regular polygon with 512 sides. Starting from a triangle, the sides of the polygon are three times a power of 2. We get the hexagon, dodecagon, 24-gon, 48-gon, and so on, all of which can be expressed as 3×2^n. Once the problem of the pentagon was solved, then polygons with sides of the form 5×2^n were also in the bag.

But not all numbers can be expressed in the form of 2^n multiplied by a whole number, for example 7, 9, or 15. Can these be constructed?

Constructing the 15-gon

As $3 \times 5 = 15$, perhaps the constructions for the triangle and pentagon can be combined in some way to produce the 15-gon. We saw earlier (pp. 22–23) how our polygons can be thought of as a series of congruent isosceles triangles meeting at a point. For 15 triangles to fit together, the angle at the vertex of each must be $360^\circ / 15 = 24^\circ$. So if we can construct an angle of 24° we are home and dry.

We start with our pentagon within its circle and, as with the hexagon (see p. 20), we use the compasses to mark the six points around the circumference.

We join alternate points to form the equilateral triangle.

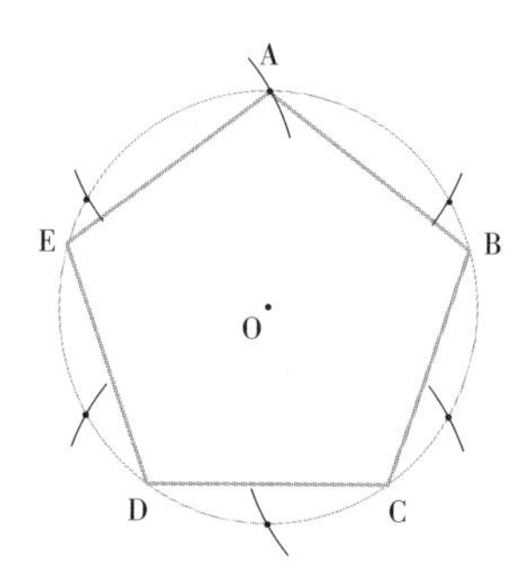

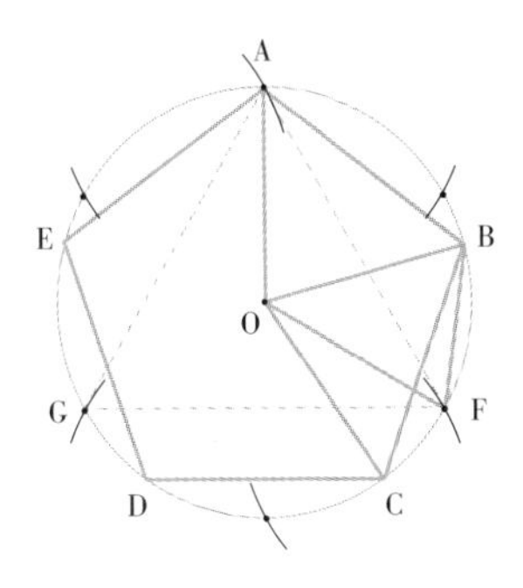

The distance CF looks as though it will fit three times between B and A. We can prove this if we can show that ∠COF is 24°. ∠AOF is 120° (it is one of the three central angles of the triangle ΔAFG) and ∠AOB is 72° (being a central angle of the pentagon ABCDE). So ∠BOF = 120° - 72° = 48°. ∠BOC is also 72°, so ∠COF = 72° - 48° = 24°.

So our hunch that CF will provide the markings from the 15-gon is correct. Setting the compasses to CF and marking this repeatedly around the circumference provides all the vertices for the 15-gon.

This approach generalizes to combining any pair of polygons through a similar construction. For example, we can superimpose an octagon on top of a pentagon to construct a 40-gon. Want a 60-gon? Construct a pentagon on top of a dodecagon.

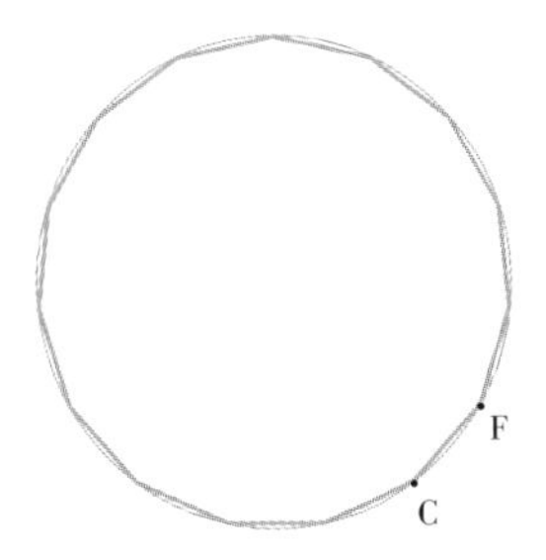

Are We There Yet?

Combining polygons in this way opens up the number of possibilities, but we still have not constructed the seven-sided heptagon. We should not be downhearted; Euclid could not construct this either.

The Prodigious Gauss

For more than 1,000 years after Euclid's death, mathematicians attempted without success to construct a heptagon. Then in 1796 Johann Gauss (see pp. 96–97) explored the problem. Gauss did not in fact construct the heptagon but he did construct a regular 17-gon—the heptadecagon—which had also stumped Euclid, and in doing so figured out that the heptagon would be impossible to construct in this way. Gauss was 17 years old at the time.

Gauss proved that a polygon with a prime number of sides, *p*, (like 7, 11, 13 or 51) can be constructed if and only if the prime number can be expressed in the form:

$$p = 2^{2^n} + 1$$

These became known as Fermat numbers and turned out not to be prime at all.

This early work convinced Gauss to become a mathematician rather than a linguist. He remained proud of this discovery throughout his life and wanted a 17-gon on his tombstone. Sadly the stonecutter refused (thinking it would look like a circle), but a memorial to Gauss in Göttingen, Germany, does have a 17-gon as its base.

Squaring the (Almost) Square

THE PROBLEM:

A classic problem from antiquity was "squaring the circle": given a circle, what size of square will have exactly the same area? In fact, this turns out to be an impossible problem, but no one knew this until pi was shown to be irrational (not able to be expressed as a fraction—see pp. 30–31). A similar challenge was whether it is possible to fill a square with other squares, all of different sizes. Although not quite a square, can you fill a 32 x 33 rectangle with the following nine square tiles? 1, 4, 7, 8, 9, 10, 14, 15, 18.

THE METHOD:

A sensible strategy is to start with the least flexible first—fit in the 18 x 18 square. Let's put that in the upper right-hand corner.

The sides of the rectangle are 32 and 33, so that means the 14 and 15 squares fit rather neatly alongside the 18.

There are 17 units to fill in along the bottom. That could be the 10 and 7 or the 8 and 9. Try the 10 and 7.

Try as we might, the other pieces cannot be fitted in around this. So try

A

18 x 18

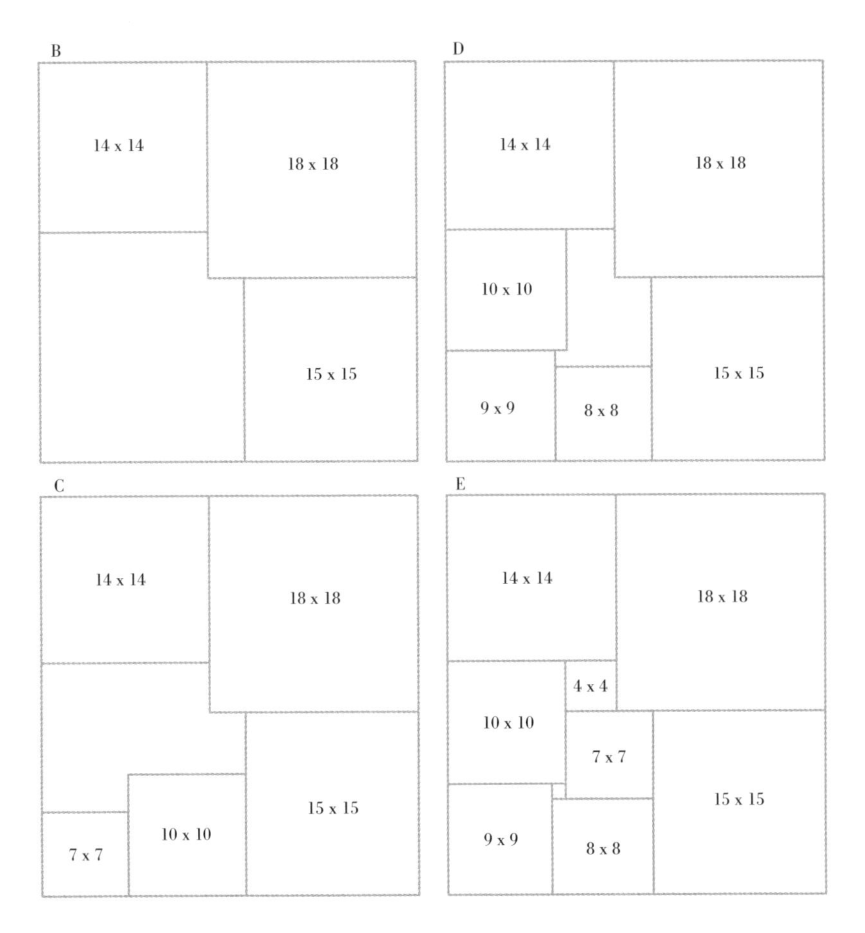

9 and 8 along the bottom. The 10 will have to go above the 9, so put the 9 in the corner and the 10 above.

We can now fit the 7, 4, and 1 squares in.

THE SOLUTION:

The squares can be fitted in as above. This "squared rectangle" puzzle and solution was first published by Zbigniew Morón in 1925. For several years no true square was found that could be filled with squares of different sizes, but Roland Sprague fitted 55 different square tiles together to make a square, publishing his solution in 1939. Theophilus Willcocks followed this in 1948 with 25 squares fitted into a square. Adrianus Duijvestijn, filling a 112 x 112 square with 20 tiles, produced the smallest version yet found. If you want to have a go, the tiles he used are: 2, 4, 6, 7, 8, 9, 11, 15, 16, 17, 18, 19, 24, 25, 29, 33, 35, 37, 42, 50.

Profile

Gottfried Leibniz

Leibniz was a German rationalist, philosopher, mathematician, and intellectual who contributed to an astonishing range of ideas in his day. In mathematics he developed new theories about topology, binary arithmetic, calculus, symbolic logic, discovery, and proof; in science he worked on force and energy, dynamics, the relativity of space and technology; and he wrote extensively on philosophy, metaphysics, and theology. As a librarian for the Duke of Brunswick, he developed the beginnings of library science, creating a book-indexing system for over 100,000 books. He also worked on an encyclopaedia of all known knowledge. Throughout his life he wrote poetry in Latin.

In his philosophical writings about the nature of God, Leibniz coined the phrase "the best of all possible worlds." He argued that God chose this world to be a balance of good and evil so that evil will be overcome and good will win through. Voltaire satirized this philosophy of optimism in his novel *Candide*, where Dr. Pangloss provides a parody of Leibniz, optimistic even under the worst conditions of life.

The Life of Leibniz

Gottfried Wilhelm Leibniz was born in Leipzig and lived from 1646 to 1716. His father, a professor of moral philosophy at the University of Leipzig, died when Leibniz was only six, so Leibniz was brought up by his mother. At an early age he studied the books of his father's extensive library, at 14 he entered the university, and by 20 he had gained a doctorate in law.

In 1667 Leibniz moved to Frankfurt to work for a private patron, Baron Johann Christian von Boineburg. He undertook a variety of projects for the Baron in science, literature, politics, and the law. He did well in court circles, and it was said of him by a contemporary, "It is rare to find learned men who are clean, do not stink, and have a sense of humor." In 1672 Leibniz moved to Paris. Here he met mathematicians, scientists, and philosophers involved in major intellectual work of the time. He traveled to London and presented a calculating machine he had designed and had built (now in the State Museum of Hanover). As a result he was made a member of the Royal Society.

After the Baron's death, Leibniz found another patron, the Duke of Brunswick, in

• Leibniz was a polymath interested in logic, mathematics, mechanics, geology, theology, law, philosophy, history, and linguistics.

"It is rare to find learned men who are clean, do not stink and have a sense of humor."

—Anonymous

Hanover. He worked as a general administrator and librarian, at the same time pursuing his own interests, studying hydraulic presses, windmills, lamps, submarines, clocks, carriages, water pumps, the binary number system, and calculus. His next patron, the Duke's brother, commissioned Leibniz to write a history of the House of Brunswick. Leibniz traveled widely in Europe under the auspices of researching this history, although he dedicated most of his time to his other studies, making contact with influential nobles in various European courts. By 1712 he was in the pay of five different courts, and too busy to serve any of them adequately. He was summoned back to Hanover by the disgruntled Duke, who required Leibniz to complete the work on the Brunswicks. Leibniz died in 1716, still working on the last of three volumes.

Dispute with Newton

In 1676 Leibniz visited the Royal Society in London and was shown an unpublished manuscript of Newton's work on calculus (which Newton called "fluxions"). Leibniz subsequently published his own developed ideas on calculus eight years later, in 1684. Newton did not publish his work on "fluxions" until 1693, and then, in a fuller version, in 1704. He and his supporters accused Leibniz of plagiarism, giving as evidence the fact that Leibniz had read and kept notes on Newton's unpublished manuscript. Leibniz claimed that he had already developed a differential calculus, and provided his workings from 1675 to prove this. It is probable that both men developed the mathematics separately, but with the knowledge and influence of the other's work. Each took the mathematics in a slightly different direction. Both men realized that finding the tangent to a curve at a particular point (differentiation) is the inverse of finding the area under a curve (integration). Leibniz provided the notation that we use today for calculus (the integral signs $\int$ and δ for differentials).

The debate continued for a long time after Leibniz's death. Newton was popular and had many supporters, and in 18th-century Britain the prevailing opinion was against Leibniz. The effect of these doubts about Leibniz, together with Voltaire's satirical portrayal of him in *Candide*, led to much of Leibniz's work being ignored until late in the 18th century. However, the discovery of calculus was revolutionary, and is vital now to physics, chemistry, engineering, economics, sociology, and any other field in which there are rates of change.

• One of the two remaining calculating machines thought to have been built during Leibniz's lifetime.

PI

From school mathematics we are all familiar with the number pi and its symbol, π. We may recall it as $22/7$ (which is only an approximation) or as around 3.141. While the Greek mathematicians knew quite a bit about π, they did not know it as a number in its own right. They understood it geometrically through the relationship between a circle and its circumference.

The Ratio of Diameter to Circumference

Geometers going way back had realized that the circumference of a circle was about three times its diameter. In the ancient Rhind papyrus, pi is calculated as equal to $16/9$ squared, which equates to 3.16049. The Babylonians had figured out that the ratio was a bit over three and worked with $3\frac{1}{8}$, which is very close to the schoolbook approximation of $3\frac{1}{7}$. In the third century CE the Chinese mathematician Liu Hui inscribed a polygon of 192 sides within a circle, and then 3072 sides, in an effort to define pi. He got a value of 3.141024.

Archimedes calculated that the value of π had to lie between $3\frac{10}{71}$ and $3\frac{1}{7}$. As we have seen, the early geometers were most at home constructing polygons with their compasses and straight edges. Archimedes used these to estimate the circumference of a circle by trapping the circle between an inscribed polygon (a polygon just fitting inside the circle) and a circumscribed polygon (a polygon that a circle will just fit within). Starting with inscribed and circumscribed hexagons is the easiest starting point (see pp. 20–21).

If the radius of the circle is 1 unit then the perimeter of the smaller inscribed hexagon is 6 units, so the

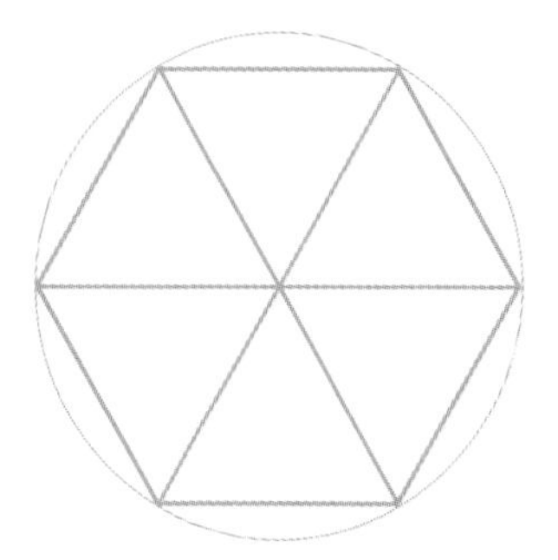

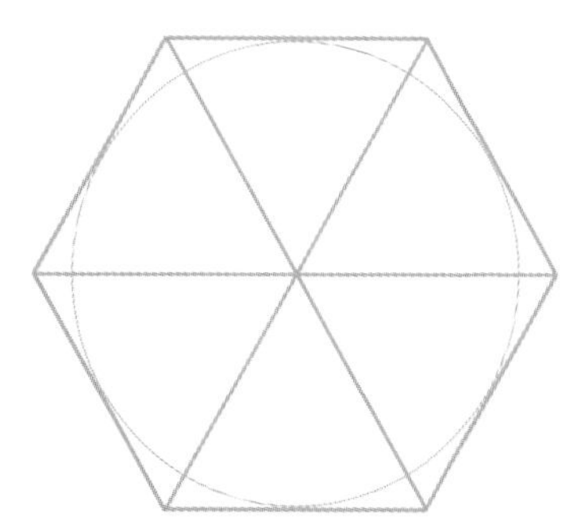

circle's circumference is greater than three times its diameter. We can use Pythagoras' theorem to calculate the length of the side of the circumscribing hexagon. If the length of the side of the larger hexagon is R, then from the fact that it just touches the circle midway along its side we can extract the following triangle:

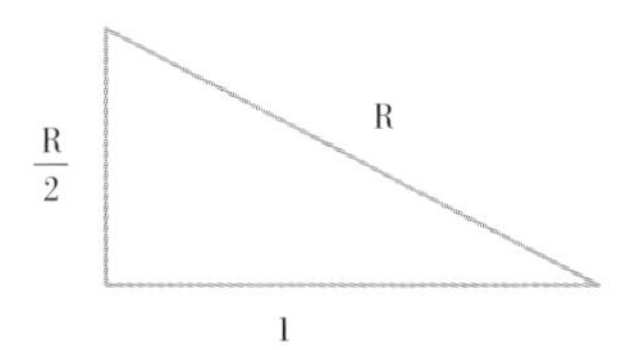

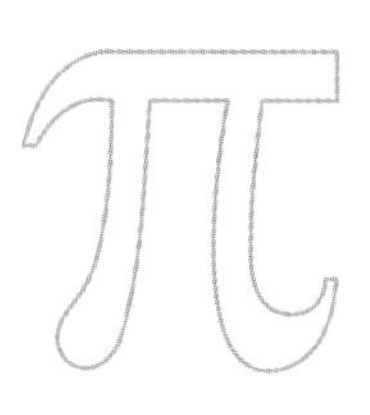

Applying Pythagoras' Theorem

$$R^2 = \left(\frac{R^2}{2}\right) + 1^2$$

$$R^2 = \left(\frac{R^2}{4}\right) + 1$$

$$\tfrac{3}{4}R^2 = 1$$

$$R^2 = \frac{4}{3}$$

$$R = \frac{2}{\sqrt{3}}$$

This gives R a value of around 1.15. So the perimeter of the circumscribing hexagon is just under 7, about 3½ times the diameter of the circle.

Archimedes was familiar with the simple process of doubling the number of sides on a regular polygon, so he continued with 12, 24, 48, and finally 96-sided constructions to get his approximation. He used a similar method to find the area of a circle (see pp. 72–72).

Modern Calculations of Pi

Computers can now calculate approximate values of pi to billions of decimal places. As pi is an irrational number, no complete and definitive decimal number will ever be obtained.

Human calculators have gone to great lengths to commit pi to memory. At the time of writing, Chao Lu from China is credited with holding the world record, having recalled 67,890 digits of pi in November 2005. It took him 24 hours and 4 minutes. Those of us with more modest ambitions and the need of a new party trick can use the following mnemonic. The number of letters in each word gives the first seven digits of pi. Since for all practical purposes a value of pi to five or six decimal places is sufficient, no need to clutter up your memory any further than this:

How I wish I could calculate pi (3.141592).

Flowerbeds

THE PROBLEM:

Jennie has a circular flowerbed with a border of small wooden logs. She decides to redesign her garden and keep a semicircular flowerbed but lay out the other half so that it is two equal smaller semicircles.

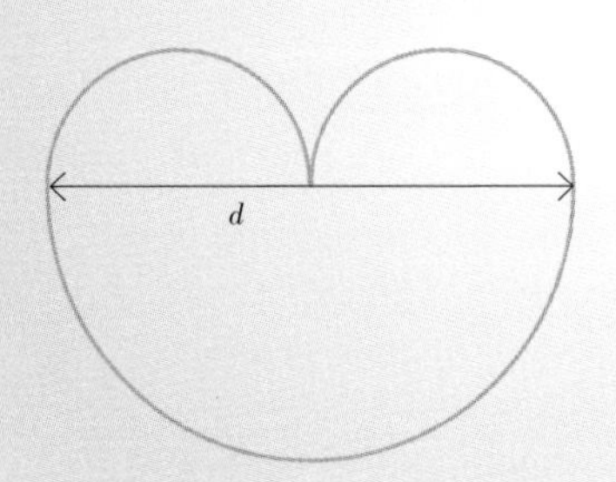

How much more edging does she need to buy to put around the perimeter of this new arrangement?

THE METHOD:

The perimeter of a circle is calculated by the formula πd, where d is the length of the circle's diameter. If the diameter of the original circle is d, then the perimeter of the semicircle is $\pi \frac{d}{2}$.

Each of the new smaller semicircles has a diameter half of the original, that is, $\frac{d}{2}$. So the perimeter of each semicircle is $(\pi \frac{d}{2}) \div 2 = \pi \frac{d}{4}$. The perimeters of the two semicircles together is $\pi \frac{d}{4} + \pi \frac{d}{4} = \pi \frac{d}{2}$.

Together with the perimeter of the large semicircle, the perimeter of the new arrangement is therefore $\pi \frac{d}{2} + \pi \frac{d}{2} = \pi d$. That's the same as the distance round the original circle. The logs that Jennie uses to border the existing circle are sufficient to go around the new arrangement without needing any more.

Maybe Jennie can be more adventurous yet. Why not put three

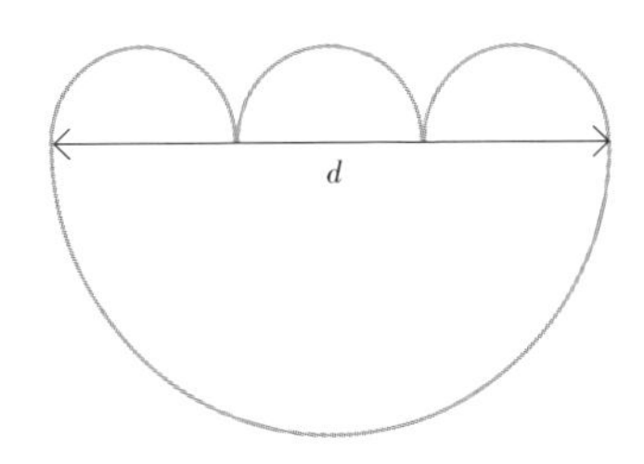

• How does the distance around the three small semicircles compare to the distance around the large semicircle?

semicircles along one half, each of a different size? Will the original length of perimeter still be preserved?

Suppose the three new semicircles have diameters $d1$, $d2$, and $d3$. The sum of their perimeters is $\pi\frac{d1}{2} + \pi\frac{d2}{2} + \pi\frac{d3}{2} = \pi\,(d1 + d2 + d3)/2$. But $d1 + d2 + d3 = d$, so the overall perimeter is $\pi\frac{d}{2} + \pi\frac{d}{2} = \pi d$. Again, this equals the perimeter or circumference of the original circle.

So why stop there? This generalizes—no matter how many semicircles are fitted along the diameter of a circle, the overall perimeter of the shape will always be the same as the perimeter of the original circle.

Imagine fitting in more and more small semicircles. Imagine fitting in an infinite number of semicircles. They will be so small that it will look as if there is just a straight line along the diameter of the large circle. Hey presto, the distance along the diameter is the same as the distance around the edge of the infinite row of semicircles. But clearly the distance around the side of the semicircle is greater than the distance straight across. A paradox.

This paradox is typical of the strange things that happen when we reach infinity. What is true in the real world may not be true at infinity!

THE SOLUTION:

Jennie can put as many semicircles along the diameter of the original circle as she wants and she will never have to buy more logs to edge the perimeter.

Exercise 5

Mind the Gap

THE PROBLEM:

Imagine, for the moment, that the planet Earth is perfectly spherical and as smooth as an enormous ping-pong ball. Imagine now that around the equator there is a ribbon that wraps perfectly all the way back to its start point.

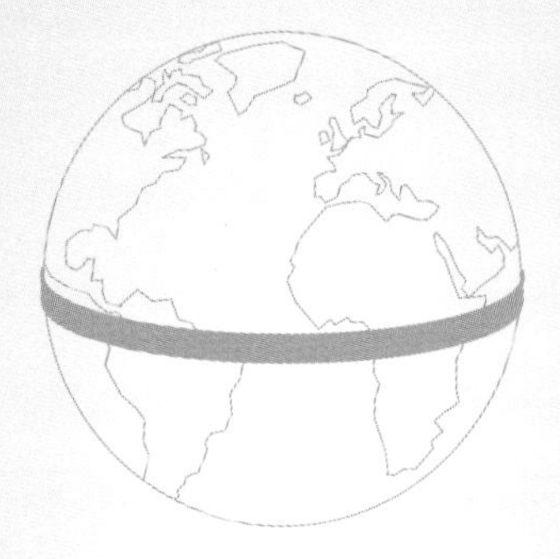

This ribbon is cut, and 3 feet of additional ribbon are spliced in. By some miraculous process, this additional 3 feet of ribbon is evenly distributed around the equator and, despite gravity, the ribbon is longer than the equator so now hovers above the equator, leaving a gap between the ribbon and Earth. The gap is a constant distance all the way around. Can anything be slid under the gap (without pulling the ribbon up to make the gap wider)? A hair, a sheet of paper, a coin, a finger, a mouse, a cat, a dog, a horse?

THE METHOD:

In comparison to the total length needed for a ribbon to go all the way round the earth—thousands of miles—three feet is a tiny amount. Although a gap will be created, intuition leads us to believe that the gap must be extremely narrow and perhaps not even a hair's breadth. Let's calculate it.

Suppose the radius of Earth is R feet (we will work in feet rather than miles so that the 3 feet does not have to be changed to a fraction of a mile). The original length of ribbon is pi times the diameter, or $\pi d = \pi(2R) = 2\pi R$.

After adding in the 3 feet, the hovering of the ribbon adds a tiny amount to the radius, an amount equal to the size of the gap. Call this tiny addition r.

We now have a radius of $R + r$ and the circumference of this is $2\pi(R + r)$. The new length was created by adding 3 feet to the old length, so:

$$2\pi(R + r) = 2\pi R + 3$$

Multiply R and r by 2π:

$$2\pi R + 2\pi r = 2\pi R + 3$$

Subtract $2\pi R$ from each side of the equation:

$$2\pi r = 3$$

$$r = \frac{3}{2\pi}$$

This gives a value of r of about 0.48 or just under half a foot. That's just less than 6 inches.

Look at the solution for r. R, the radius of Earth, is not used in the final calculation. The gap, r, is the same size irrespective of the radius of the original sphere. Put a ribbon around a tennis ball, add three feet to it and the gap created will be exactly the same size as if you had done this to the Sun.

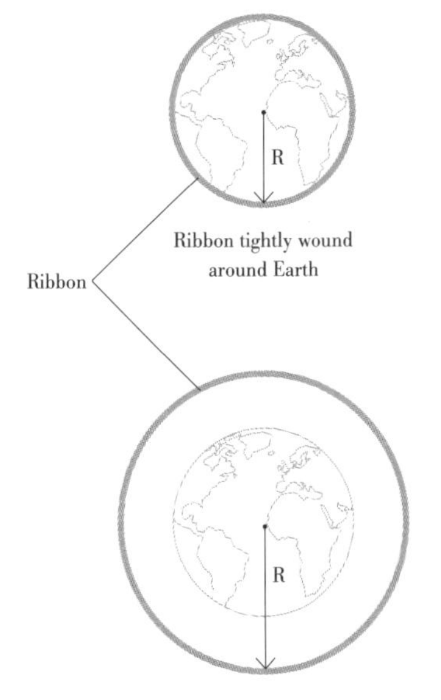

Ribbon length increased by 3 feet. Find r.

THE SOLUTION:

Adding 3 feet to a ribbon around a sphere creates a gap of around 6 inches, irrespective of the size of the sphere.

Profile

René Descartes

René Descartes was a French philosopher, mathematician, and scientist, known as the father of modern philosophy as well as for his famous quote, *cogito ergo sum* ("I think, therefore I am").

His significant work in mathematics, *La Géométrie*, shows how to analyze geometric shapes using algebra, that is, using coordinates to map points on a plane. We now call this Cartesian geometry, after Descartes. The name "Cartesian" comes from the Latin name that Descartes used for himself: Renatus Cartesius.

The Life of Descartes

Descartes lived from 1596 to 1650. He was born in La Haye, a town near Tours in France, that was renamed "Descartes" in 1967. His mother died when he was one. Because his health was delicate as a child, he was allowed stay in bed until 11 each morning. He continued this habit throughout his life, even at school.

He was educated by Jesuits and then at the University of Poitiers, where he graduated with a law degree. Instead of becoming a lawyer, he joined the army. In 1617 he was employed by Prince Maurice of Orange and moved to Breda in the Dutch Republic, and then to Bavaria to take part in the Thirty Years' War.

During 1618 he had a series of vivid dreams that he took as a sign that he should spend his life pursuing wisdom and knowledge. He used all his spare time in the army studying mathematics, mechanics, and philosophy. While in Breda he worked with Isaac Beekman, a medical student and mathematician. Beekman's diaries note the extraordinary range of ideas Descartes was working on: the mathematics of tuning lute strings; using algebra to calculate the displacement of a heavy object in water; graphs to predict the increased speed of a pencil falling in a vacuum; how a spinning top stays upright; and other ideas. He was 22 when he wrote to Beekman saying that all geometry could be expressed in axes, lines, and curves.

He resigned his commission in 1621 and spent the next five years traveling around Europe, mostly studying mathematics, and meeting the leading intellectuals of the day. He sold his family property and invested the proceeds, which provided him

- **Descartes' works**

His first major work was on science, called Le Monde, *and based on the contentious works of Copernicus. Descartes was about to publish this in 1634 when he heard of the arrest of Galileo. For his own safety he suppressed the publication. In 1637 he published* Discourse on Method *(a framework for the natural sciences), with* Optics, Meteorology, *and* La Géométrie. *In* Meditations, *1641, he outlined his philosophical views. He wrote many other papers and books on various subjects: the human body, musical instruction, mechanics, and many more.*

with an income for life. In 1628 he settled in the Dutch Republic, where he lived for the next 20 years, writing prolifically.

He died of pneumonia while working as a teacher to Queen Christina of Sweden in 1650. She made him rise at 6 instead of 11 to give her lessons, and it is said this made him ill. But probably he caught the infection from a friend staying with him.

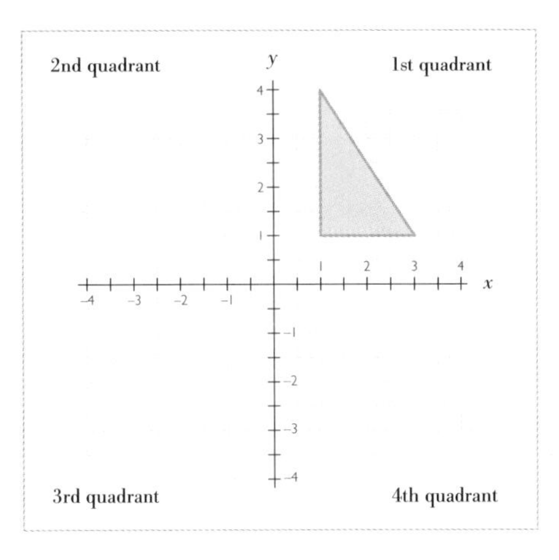

Descartes' Geometry

Descartes proposed to bring together algebra and geometry, which, at the time, were considered quite separate disciplines. In his writing he introduced analytic geometry, or Cartesian geometry, where geometric shapes were converted into algebraic equations. His ideas contributed to those of Leibniz and Newton, and helped toward the development of calculus.

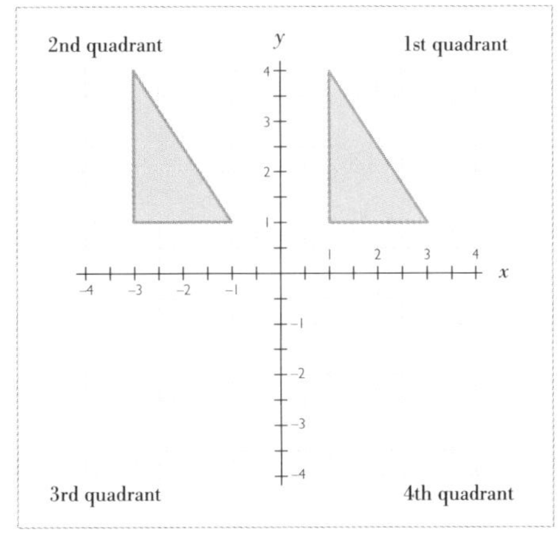

Cartesian geometry uses a number line, with another placed perpendicular to it, to describe plane shapes. Using algebra, you can make changes to a plane shape. You can translate it (move it in a straight line), rotate it, make a reflection of it, and scale it (make it larger or smaller), all using the coordinate notation. A simple example (shown opposite) is to translate the green triangle to the position of the blue triangle.

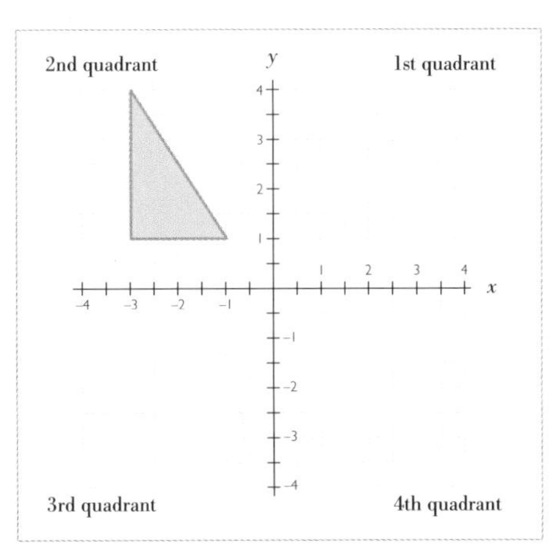

To move the green triangle (1,1) (3,1) (1,4) in a straight line, change each pair of coordinates in the same way: (1 + X, 1 + Y) (3 + X, 1 + Y) (1 + X, 4 + Y). The *x* coordinates all change by X, and the *y* coordinates all change by Y. To move the green triangle to the position of the blue triangle, we don't change the position on the *y*-axis, but we move the triangle 4 points to the left. Left is in a negative direction, so X is –4 and Y is 0.

CONICS

The light cast on the walls and ceilings from a circular lampshade are familiar to us. The lamp will create a larger circle on the ceiling, but tilt the lamp and the circle moves out of being "true." Near a wall, two curved images are projected—one above the lamp and one below. Neither of these are circles, although they are the result of the circle of light from the top or bottom of the lamp. They are conic sections and a study of these from around 800 CE bore fruits in mechanics and astronomy.

Conic Sections

We call these curves conics because we create them by slicing through a double cone. To visualize a double cone, imagine two ice-cream cones joined at their vertices (see the diagrams below). Slice through the cones with a horizontal plane and we get the circle. As we tilt the plane we are slicing with, we get a closed oval: the ellipse. A circle is in fact a special ellipse.

To create ellipses, we can only slice through one half of the pair of cones. If we increase the "tilt" of the plane so that we slice through both cones, we get two cut-off ellipses. Unlike the ellipses, which are closed curves, these cuts create a curve that is in two parts; each of which extends infinitely. Together this pair of curves is the hyperbola.

In addition to the planes that create ellipses and hyperbolas, there is a further plane that slices through one half of the cone only (see diagram below-right). This creates an open curve that extends to infinity: the parabola. The planes producing parabolas are parallel to the face of the cone.

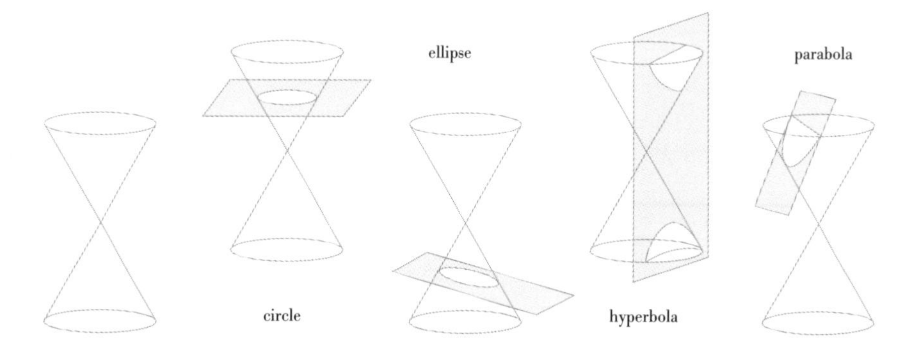

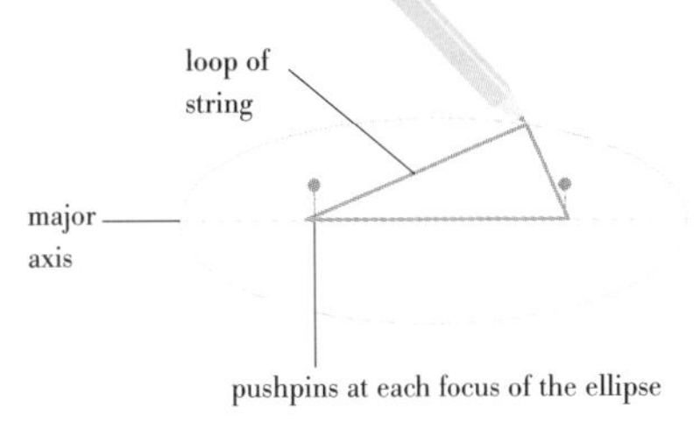

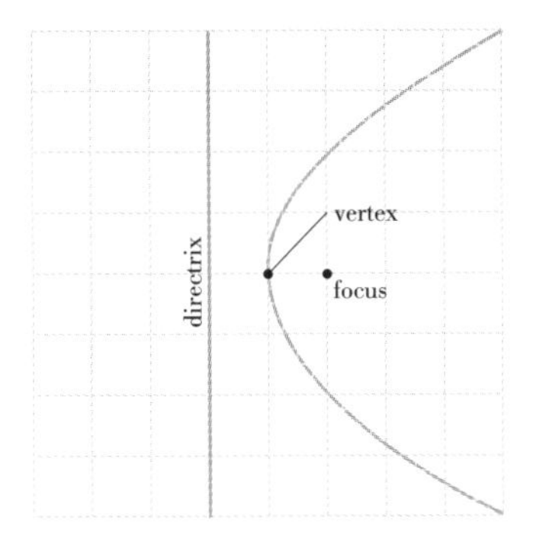

• Along a parabola, the locus will always be equidistant from the focus and directrix.

Loci

The conics can also be described (and created) by following the movement—the locus—of a point in the plane. Put two pushpins in a board, place a circle of string around them and pull the loop taut with a pencil. Keeping the string taut and moving the pencil to draw a curve will produce an ellipse.

As the length of the string does not change, all points along the perimeter of the ellipse are the same distance from the midpoint between the two pins. This distance is expressed as the sum of the distance from the two pins. The points marked by the pins are called the foci of the ellipse. Move these points together and the ellipse looks more and more like a circle, until at the point where the two foci coincide it is a circle.

A different set-up produces the parabola. The locus that produces a parabola is the result of a point moving so that its distance from a second point (the focus) always equals its perpendicular distance from a specific line (called the directrix).

A parabola is easy to create: simply throw a ball in an arc toward a partner. Mirrors or satellite dishes are parabolic and make use of the literal focus: light or radio signals bouncing off the inside of a parabolic dish all meet at the focus.

Catena

If you come to a track closed off by a chain or rope hanging between two points, the curve of the chain looks remarkably like a parabola.

Galileo claimed that this would indeed be a parabola, but the German mathematician Joachim Jungius showed in 1669 that Galileo was incorrect. What the curve actually was became the object of a public challenge posed by Johann Bernoulli in 1690 that was solved by a quartet of mathematicians (including Bernoulli) a year later. The curve became known as the catenaria (from the Latin for chain; *catena*) and was latterly to become called catenary when linked to designing bridges.

• The curve created by a hanging chain looks like a parabola but is subtly different.

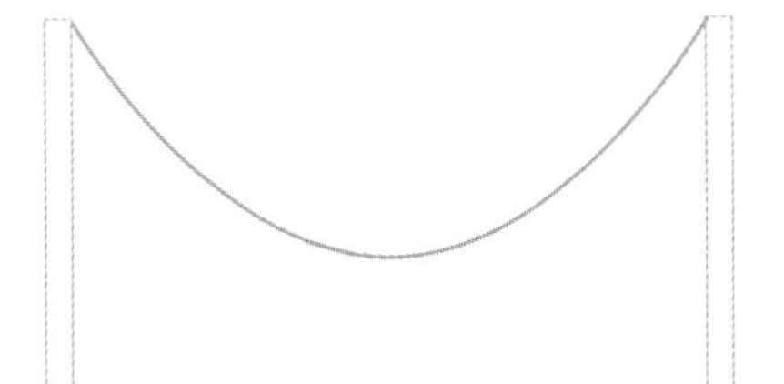

Chapter

Jewels in the Crown

The astronomer Johannes Kepler claimed that there are two great treasures in geometry: the theorem of Pythagoras and the golden ratio. "The first may be compared to a measure of gold, the second to a precious jewel." We explore these two treasures in this chapter.

GEOMETRICAL STABILITY

Our built environment looks as though it is constructed from objects with verticals and horizontals—bricks, windows, lamp posts. So much so that it appears that rectangles are the most basic of geometric shapes. But it is the humbler triangle that holds our structures together.

The Strength of the Triangle

The triangle, made up by joining struts together, is the only simple structure whose shape is not deformed when pressure is applied to its corners. This is easily demonstrated with straws. Three straws joined to make a triangle (you can do this by threading fine string or wool through and tying it off) create a stable shape—try to change it by moving one of the corners and you cannot. Four straws joined to make a square are far from stable—the square is easily pushed out of being "true" and easily deformed into a whole range of rhombi (quadrilaterals with four equal sides, the square being a special case when the angles of the rhombus are all right angles). The only way to make the square stable is to put in a diagonal, essentially turning the structure into two triangles.

Most of our buildings cover up the basic triangular structures, but there are two places where the structure is transparent: pylons and cranes. Such is some folks' fascination with these that there used to be a "pylon of the month" website—sadly now gone to the internet in the sky.

Similarity and Congruence

Are the two triangles on the opposite page the same? The answer depends on what we mean by "the same." They are both equilateral triangles, so in the sense of being the same "type" of triangle, the answer is yes. If you imagine cutting them out and putting one on top of the

• The square is not a stable structure and is easily bent out of being "true."

• All equilateral triangles are mathematically similar to each other.

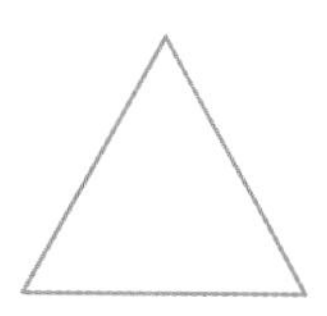

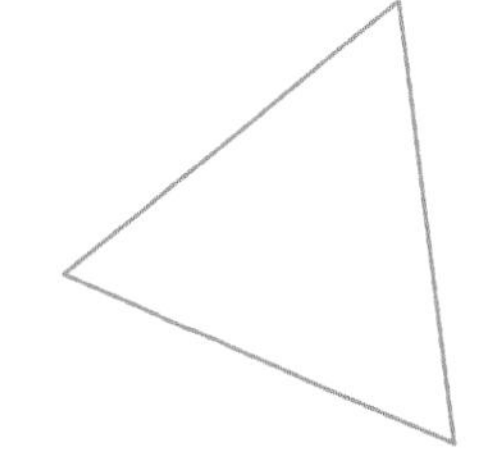

other then it is clear that one is larger than the other and so they are not the same in the sense of being identical. (A philosopher might argue that as there are clearly two triangles and not one, then asking if they are "the same" is nonsense, but we won't go down that road.) In order to clarify whether two triangles are "sort of" the same, mathematicians distinguish between shapes being similar or congruent.

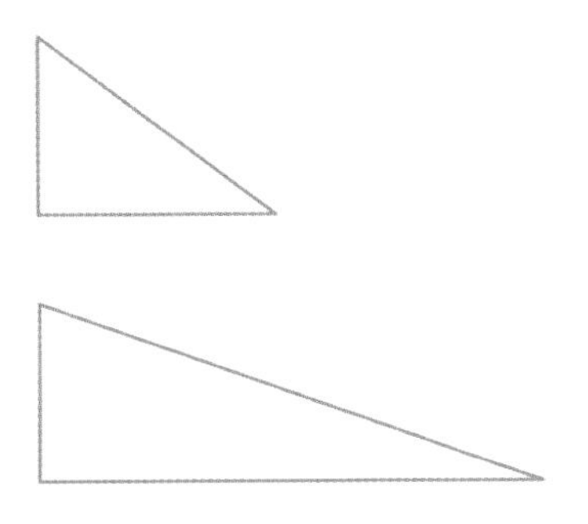

• Although these triangles are similar in the sense that they both have a right angle, they are not mathematically similar.

Shapes are mathematically congruent if they match each other in all respects, if they could be positioned on top of each other and provide a perfect fit. (Such positioning might include having to flip one of the shapes over, so mirror reflections count as congruent.)

Shapes are mathematically similar if one can be enlarged or reduced in size without altering its proportions and would then be congruent to the other shape. An intuitive way of thinking about this is to imagine the optical trick of holding up the smaller shape and being able to position it so that it exactly fits onto the vision of the other shape (just as you can hold up a finger and "see" the finger as being as long as the side of a building). The use of the word "similar" mathematically is more precise than everyday use. We might say that the triangles above are "similar" in that they both contain a right angle, but they are not mathematically similar: one cannot be "shrunk" to fit exactly onto the other without altering the proportions of the sides. All circles are similar to each other, as are all squares.

• **Geometrical stability**

The suitability of the triangle for forming stable structures has been long recognized, particularly in the design of tents. Geodesic domes are constructed out of triangular elements that are connected in such a way that stress is distributed across the whole structure. Computer-assisted design now allows accurate calculation of the dimensions required to construct buildings of increasing structural complexity.

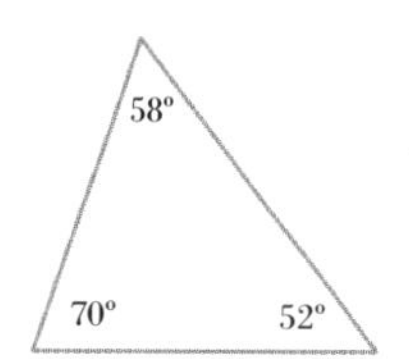

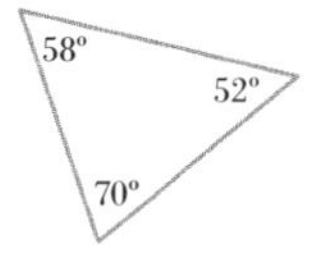

• Establishing whether two triangles are similar is simply a case of comparing the angles.

Checking Triangles Are Similar

This is easy. If the angles of two triangles are the same, then irrespective of the lengths of the sides, the triangles are similar. We only need to check that a pair of triangles has two pairs of matching angles; since the sum of the angles is 180°, the third angle pair must automatically match. And it doesn't matter where the angles are positioned in the triangle—flipping or rotating one of the triangles means we can always arrange the angles in the same order.

Checking Triangles Are Congruent

This is a bit trickier. Turns out that there are four tests that need to be applied, depending on what information is available about the two triangles. The tests are: side, side, side (SSS); side, angle, side (SAS); angle, side, angle (ASA); and right angle, hypotenuse, side (RHS).

SSS

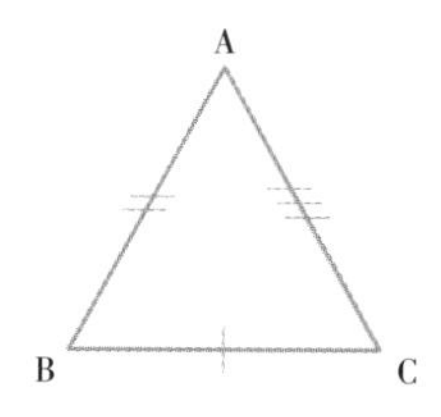

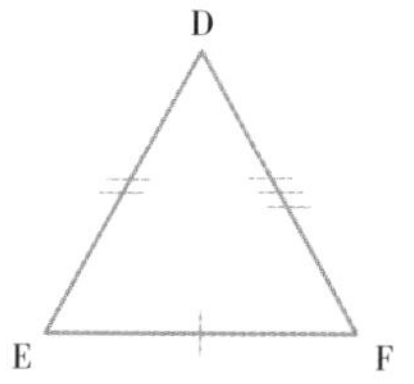

CONGRUENT QUADRILATERALS

Traditionally, the tests for geometrical congruence have been limited to the study of a single shape—when you studied it in school, the chances are that it involved working with triangles. Despite what this limited focus may imply, any pair of shapes can be congruent. As we shall see, if the three pairs of sides of two triangles match in length then the triangles must be congruent. There is an important exception, however: two quadrilateral triangles can have sides of the same length and not be congruent.

If we know that the lengths of the three sides of each triangle are the same, then the triangles must be congruent.

SAS

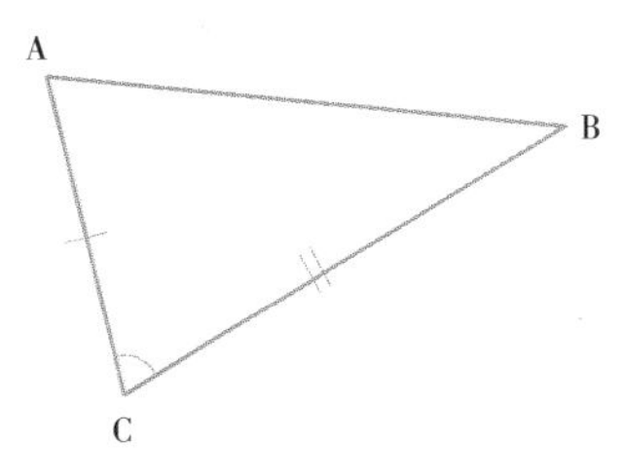

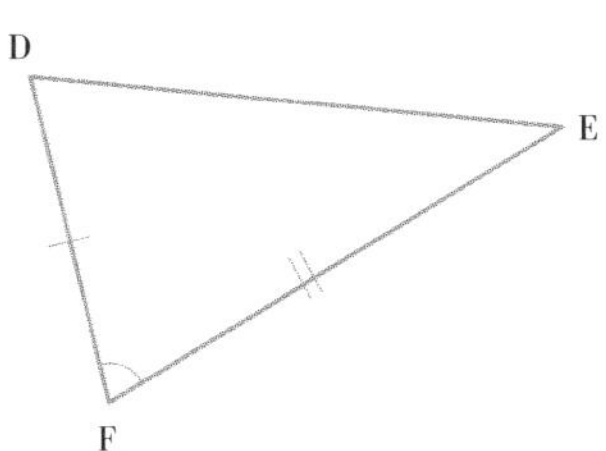

If we know that two triangles have two matching pairs of sides AND the same angle between the pair of sides, then the triangles must be congruent.

ASA

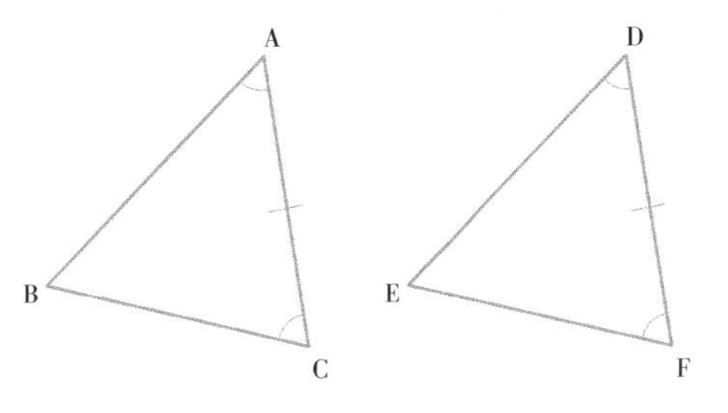

If we know that two triangles have two matching angles AND the sides between the pair of angles are the same length, then the triangles must be congruent.

RHS

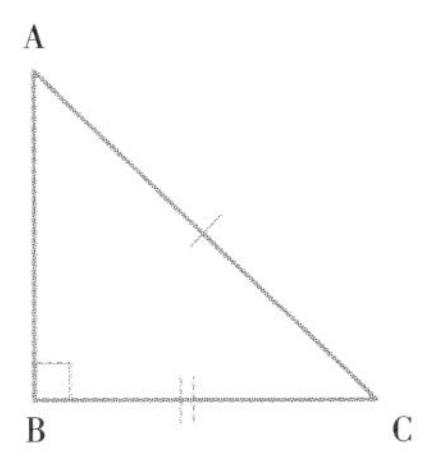

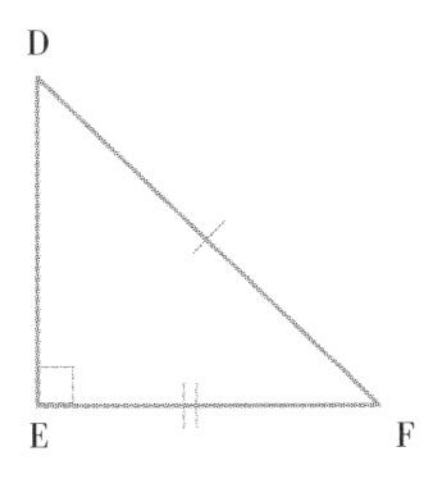

If we know that two triangles have a right angle AND their hypotenuses (sides opposite the right angle) are the same length AND another side the same length, then the triangles must be congruent.

These tests for congruence are at the heart of establishing many geometrical proofs, as we will see in the following exercises. The important thing to note in using these is that we do not actually need to know the size of the angles or the lengths of the sides, just that, logically, they can be shown to be the same.

Exercise 6

Round the Garden

THE PROBLEM:

Felicity is landscaping her garden. She has three shady oak trees and wonders if she could build a circular paved area with the trees on its circumference. Can Felicity construct such a circle and where should she mark its center? She only has a straight edge, compasses, and length of rope to work with.

THE METHOD:

There are two parts to this problem. The first is an existence problem: given three points (three trees in this case), does a circle always exist with these three points on its circumference? The second is a construction problem: if the circle does exist, how can we construct it?

We run into difficulties with the existence problem if our three points are in a straight line (collinear). A moment's thought experiment trying to picture a circle passing through three collinear points should convince you that this is impossible.

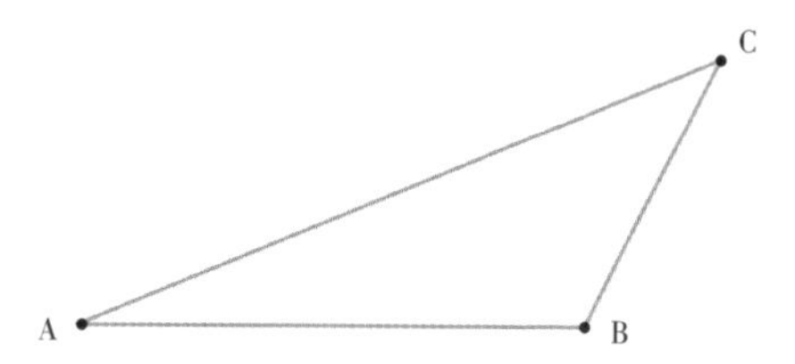

What if our three points are non-collinear? Let's represent our points (or trees) by A, B, C and join them by straight-line segments to make a triangle.

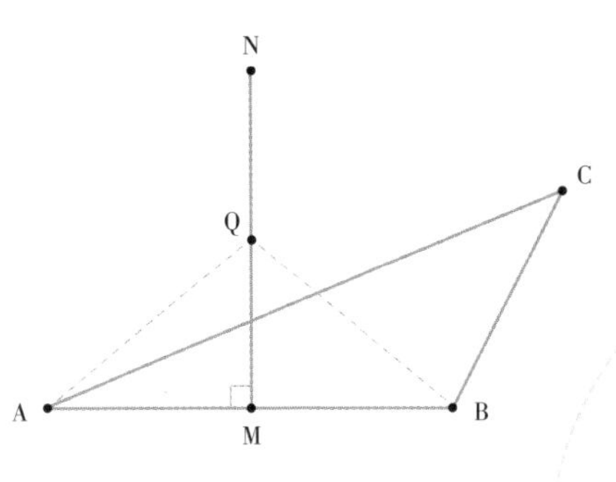

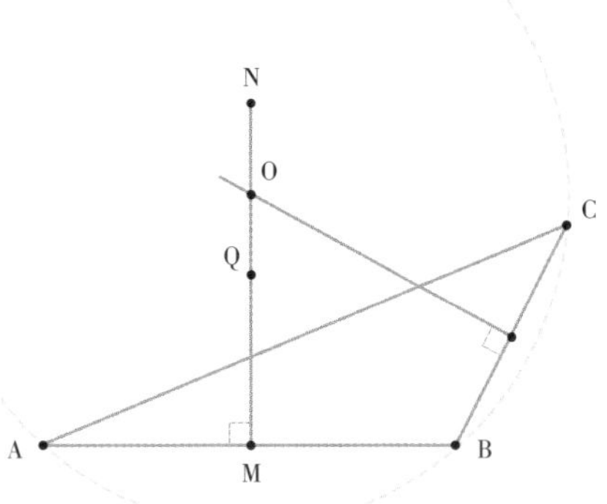

Focusing only on side AB, we can construct a perpendicular bisector to it (see pp. 14–15). Let's call that line MN. Any point on MN (call it Q) will be as far from A is it is from B. It looks that way in the diagram above and we can prove it by looking for congruent triangles (see pp. 44–45). ΔAMQ and ΔBMQ are congruent (SAS), so AQ must be the same length as BQ.

So a circle with center Q and radius AQ will pass through both A and B. All we need to do now is also include C. To do that we carry out a similar construction on side BC. The two perpendicular bisectors will cross somewhere; call it point O. As before, OB = OC and, since OA = OB, a circle with center O and radius OA will pass through A, B and C. Note that in solving the existence problem we have also solved the construction problem. We have proved that Felicity can construct a circle with the trees on the circumference (as long as the trees are not collinear) and also how to construct it. Finding the center of the circle requires only a straight edge and pair of compasses. And the rope? Felicity needs that to draw out the circle.

THE SOLUTION:

The circle constructed in this way is known as a triangle's circumcircle and point O is the triangle's circumcenter.

Waste Not

THE PROBLEM:

Robert is a furniture-maker. A client brought him a coffee table with a triangular top and asked him to recycle the top and cut it to make the largest possible circular tabletop. Using a straight edge and pair of compasses, how does Robert find and mark out the circle he needs?

THE METHOD:

Clearly, Robert can cut a circle, but how to make it as large as possible is not obvious. The key lies in bisecting the angles of the triangle.

Let's label the corners of our tabletop A, B, C and start off by bisecting A (see p. 15).

Is it the case that any point, Q say, on that bisector is the same distance from the sides AB and AC? Intuitively it feels as if this should be so, but let's ground our intuition in proof. The distance from Q to a side is the length of the line from Q that is perpendicular to the side. We can construct the two distances and label some angles.

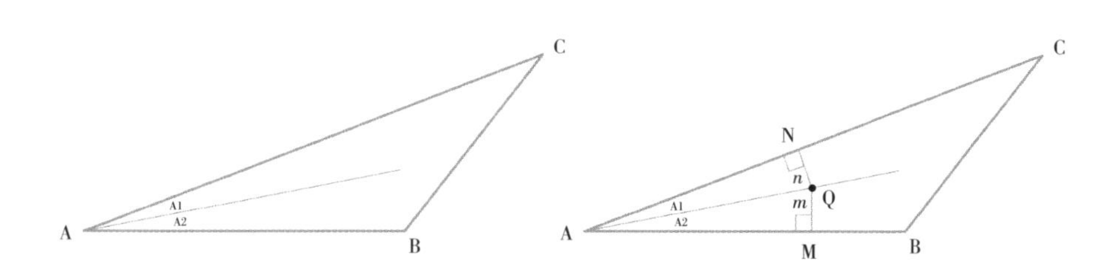

Is QM equal to QN? Congruent triangles come to our rescue. Each triangle has a right angle, so $m = 180^\circ - 90^\circ - a_1$ (since the angles of a triangle add up to 180°) and $n = 180^\circ - 90^\circ - a_2$. But $a_1 = a_2$, hence $m = n$. AQ has to be the same length in the triangles ΔADQ and ΔAEQ as it is a common side. Therefore ΔADQ and ΔAEQ are congruent triangles (ASA) and QM = QN.

We now bisect B and label where it crosses the bisector of A as the point I.

Since I lies on the bisector of B it is the same distance from BC as it is from BA and so IF = ID. We know from above that ID = IE. So IF = ID. We will leave you to think about why ΔCEI and ΔCFI must be congruent (it is based on SAS) and hence establish that $c_1 = c_2$.

The important thing that we have shown is that point I is the same distance from each of the sides of the triangle, so a circle can be drawn with center I that just touches each side. This is the largest that can fit in the triangle.

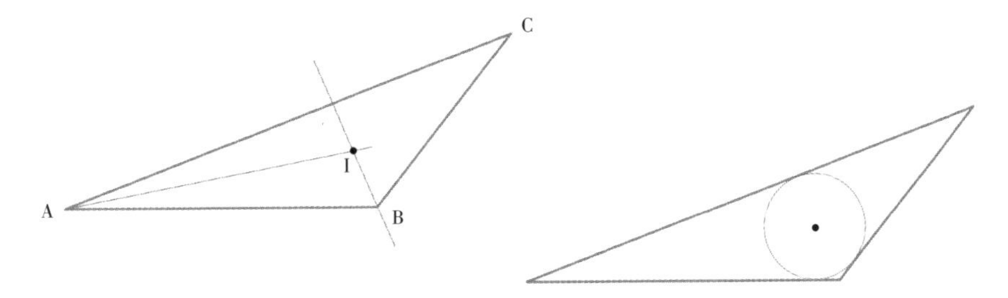

Intuitively it feels as if the line from C to I should bisect C. Putting in the distances from I to each side allows us to check this out.

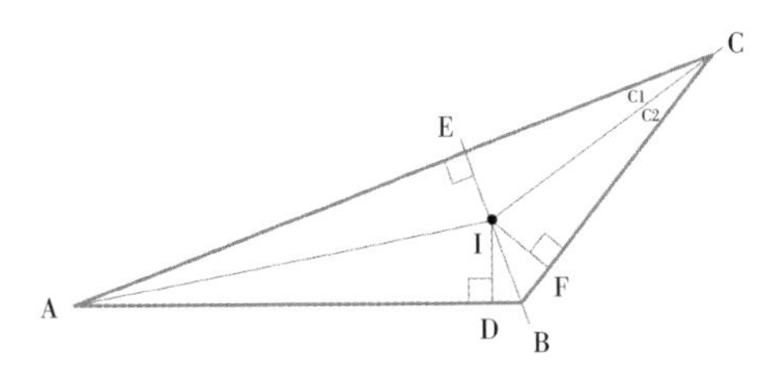

THE SOLUTION:

The circle constructed in this way is known as the triangle's incircle and point I is the triangle's incenter.

EULER'S LINE

In the preceding two exercises we found two important points within any triangle: O, the circumcenter of a triangle (the center of the circle that the triangle neatly sits within, shown on the diagram below-left) and I, the incenter (the center of the circle that neatly sits within the circle). The circumcenter of a triangle is the point of intersection of the three perpendicular bisectors of the sides. The incenter of a triangle is the point of intersection of the three angle bisectors.

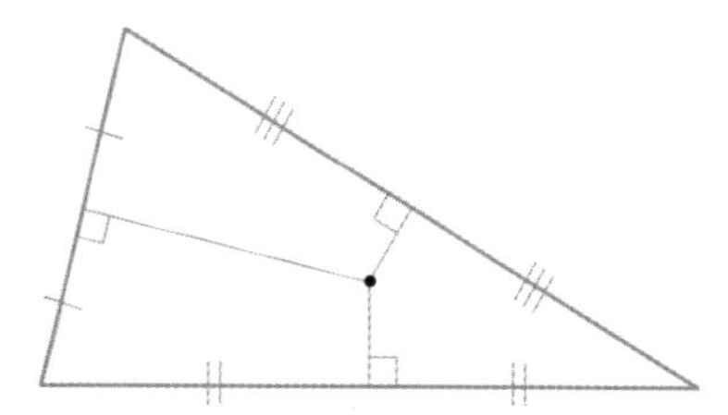

• O, the circumcenter, where the perpendicular bisectors of the sides meet.

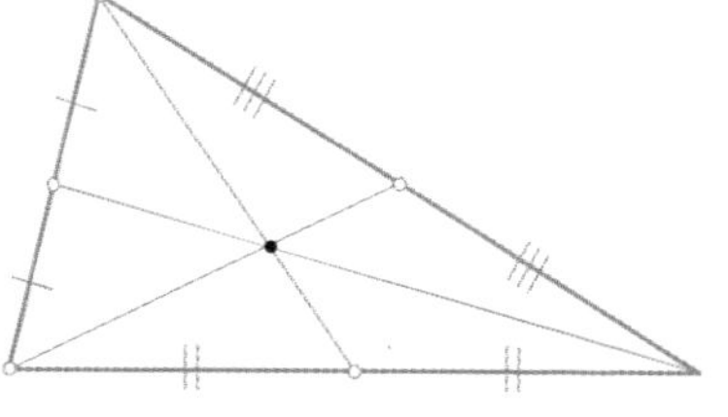

• G, the centroid, where lines joining each angle to the midpoint of the opposite side meet.

These are not the only "centers" that any triangle can have: mathematically there are hundreds. Two other centers turn out to be particularly mathematically interesting.

Suppose you have a triangle cut out of a piece of card that you want to suspend from the ceiling on a piece of cord. Where would you attach the cord so that the triangle would lie horizontally when suspended? Or, another way to think of this is: where would you place a pencil point underneath a cut-out triangle to "balance" the triangle on the upright pencil?

The point we are trying to find here is the center of gravity of the triangle, known as the "centroid" of the triangle and generally referred to as G (see the diagram above). The centroid of a triangle is the point of intersection of each of the three lines that run from the vertices of a triangle to the midpoint of their opposite sides. These lines are called medians.

To complete our set of "centers," we can also construct the three lines from each vertex that are perpendicular to the opposite side. These lines are called altitudes. As you might expect, these three lines all intersect at one point, the "orthocenter" of the triangle, generally called H.

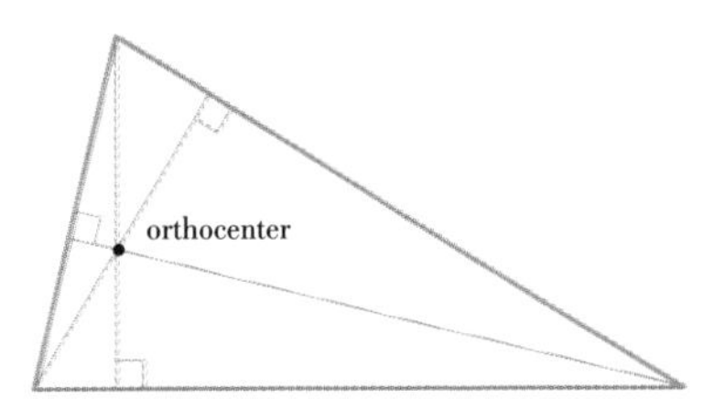

• H, the orthocenter, where the altitudes of each side intersect.

Three of these centers—O, the circumcenter, G, the centroid, and H, the orthocenter—turn out all to lie on a straight line. This is called the Euler line. The Euler line of a triangle is a line that passes through the orthocenter, the circumcenter and the centroid of a triangle.

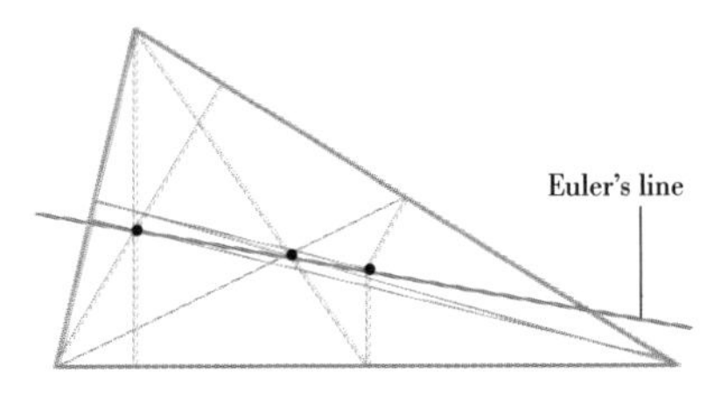

In an equilateral triangle, these centers all converge onto one point, so an equilateral triangle has an unambiguous center; this is called the center of an equilateral triangle.

Euler (see pp. 132–133) also explored the relationship between circles that circumscribe and inscribe a triangle, and circles bounded by the external extensions of the sides of the triangle.

KARL WILHELM FEUERBACH

Karl Wilhelm Feuerbach made perhaps the most startling discovery in 1882. A high school teacher, Feuerbach investigated nine points that lie in any triangle:

- The three midpoints of the sides.
- The feet of the three altitudes on each side.
- The midpoints of the three lines joining the orthocenter (H) to the vertices.

These nine points look randomly scattered:

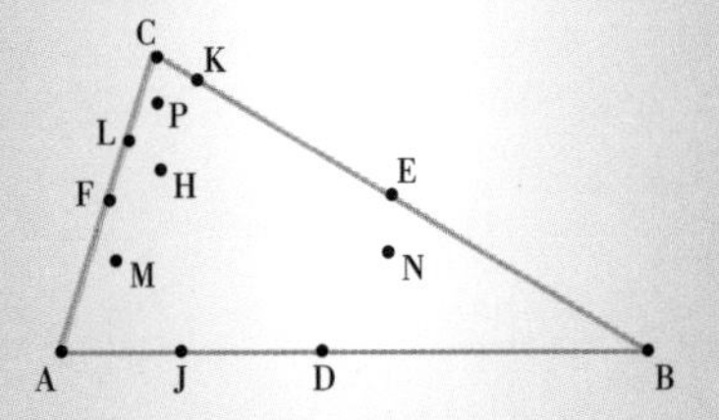

Feuerbach found that actually all nine points lie on the circumference of a circle. And, surprise, surprise, the center of this nine-point circle lies on the Euler line.

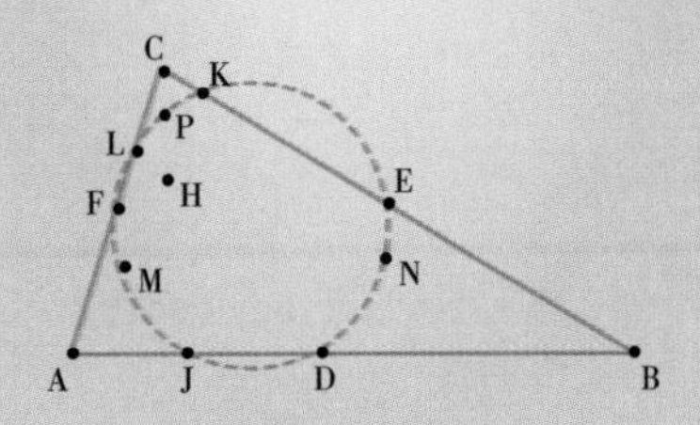

Exercise 8

Desert Island Bliss

THE PROBLEM:

Sheila is a keen swimmer. Winning the lottery means that she can make her dream come true of buying an island and building a house on it. The island that Sheila buys is close to being an equilateral triangle. Sheila wants to go swimming off each of the three beaches on her island an equal number of times. She wonders where to build her house so that over time the distances she travels to the three beaches are kept to a minimum. Where should Sheila build her house?

THE METHOD:

Setting Sheila's situation up as a mathematical model, the problem can be restated as finding the point within an equilateral triangle that minimizes the sum of the distances to each side of the triangle. The distance from a point to a side is the length of the line from the point and perpendicular to the side. So, taking any point (P) inside the triangle, diagrammatically Sheila's problem looks like this:

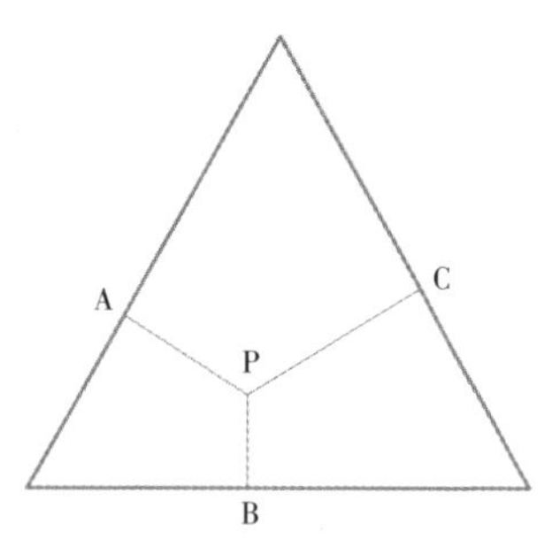

The problem is where to position P so that the sum of PA, PB, and PC is as small as possible.

By drawing lines parallel to each of the sides of the triangle, these three distances can be placed within three smaller equilateral triangles.

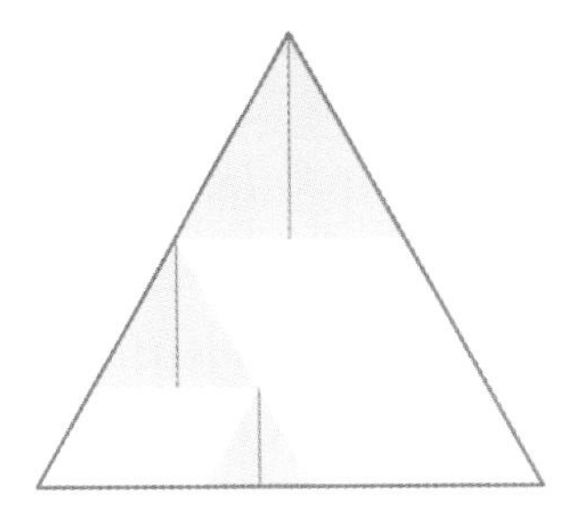

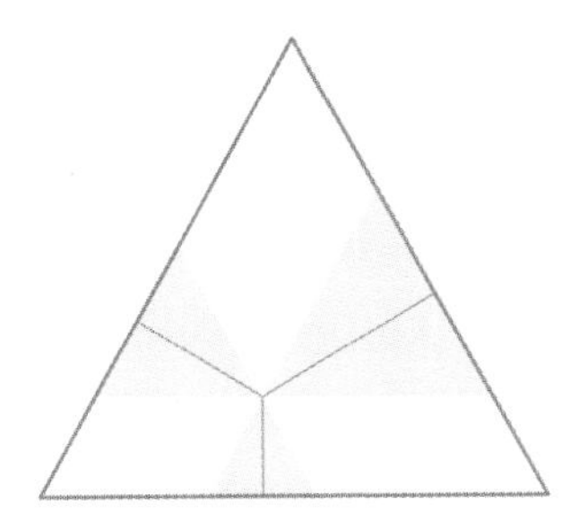

Leaving two of these triangles in place, the third can be slid up the side of the triangle to fit in the top and marry up with the triangle below it.

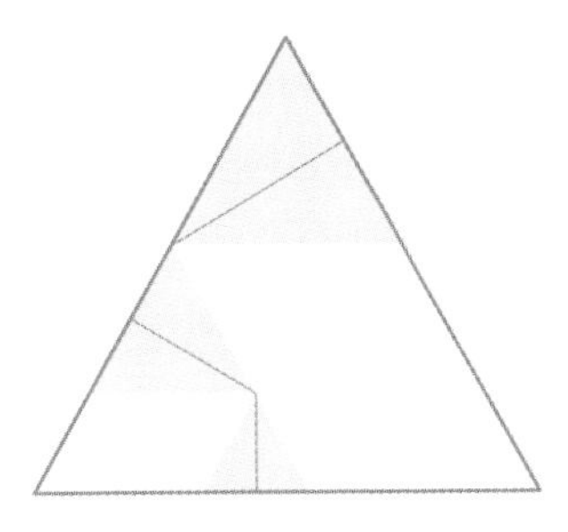

Rotating two of the three triangles so that the lines indicating the distance from P are all vertical, it becomes clear that the sum of these three distances is equal to the height of the triangle.

But we started with P as any point within the triangle, so wherever P is placed, the sum of the distances to the sides of the triangle will always be the same.

In other words, it doesn't actually matter where Sheila builds her house; the sum of the distances to the three beaches will always be the same. She can build it in the spot that has the best view.

THE SOLUTION:

The result that the sum of the perpendicular distances to the sides from any point in an equilateral triangle is equal to the height of the triangle is known as Viviani's theorem, named after the Italian scientist and mathematician Vincenzo Viviani. He established this result around 1660, but the proof without words presented here was developed by Ken-ichiroh Kawasaki in 2005. The result also holds for any equiangular or equilateral polygon.

PYTHAGORAS' THEOREM

A mathematician once noted that anyone who thinks mathematics is difficult simply hasn't appreciated how complicated the real world is. Pythagoras' theorem marks a mathematical moment of certainty in a complicated world.

Picture two squares, A and B, different in size, and hinged together. A third square, C, is constructed so that two of its corners match up with corners from A and B.

A and B are fixed in size but can be rotated together or apart about their hinge. C is "stretchy" and changes size as A and B move. When the angle between A and B is large, the area of C is considerably bigger than the areas of A and B put together. With A and B close together, the area of C then becomes much smaller than the total of the areas of A and B.

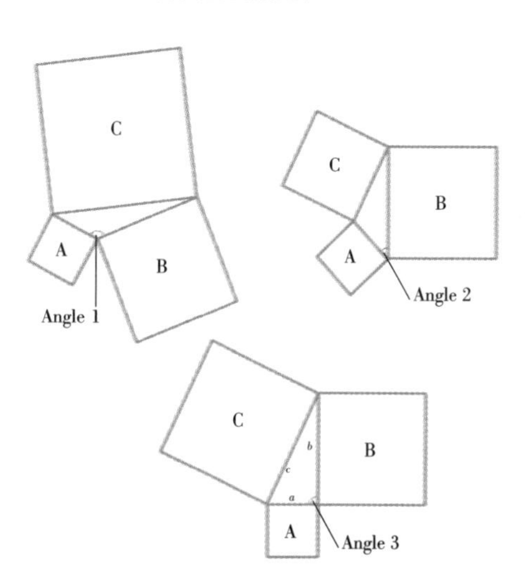

As A and B move together or apart, the area of C changes smoothly, shrinking or growing. From a position where C's area is greater than that of A plus B to a position where it is smaller than this sum, there is a moment, and one moment only, when the area of C must be precisely equal to the sum of the areas of A and B. That moment just happens to be when A and B are at right angles to each other.

If the sides of A, B, and C have lengths a, b and c respectively, then at that moment of balance a right-angled triangle is formed between the squares with c as the hypotenuse. Hence:

The square on the hypotenuse is equal to the sum of the squares on the other two sides. Or, $c^2 = a^2 + b^2$

Proving Pythagoras' Theorem

Of course, this thought experiment does not prove that the equality occurs when A and B are at a right angle to each other—it just looks as if that is the case.

There are a multitude of proofs of the theorem of Pythagoras, including one by our friend Euclid, but here are two of our favorite, more unusual, ones.

Proof Without Words

These diagrams from China provide a wordless, visual proof. Before reading on, you might like to think about how the two images can help you "see" Pythagoras' theorem in them.

First, note that the area of each square is the same. Second, that there are four identical right-angled triangles in each square. Removing these triangles from each square must leave equal areas behind. So the sum of the areas of the two squares embedded in P must be the same as the area of the "tilted" square in Q. These three squares fit the sides of the triangle. Bingo. Pythagoras' theorem.

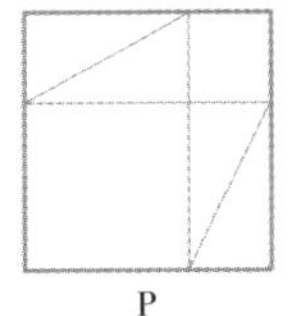
P

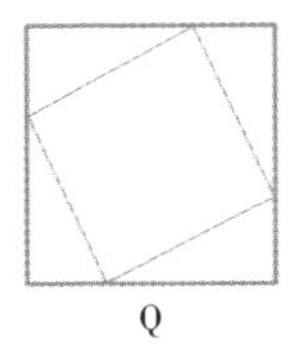
Q

JAMES GARFIELD

Graduating in 1856, Garfield was going to be a mathematics teacher but got involved in politics and was eventually elected the 20th President of the United States. Perhaps he should have stuck with mathematics, as he was shot after only four months in office. The bullet did not immediately kill him, but he died from a punctured liver sustained in the subsequent medical care.

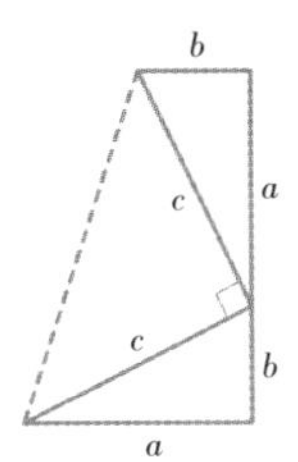

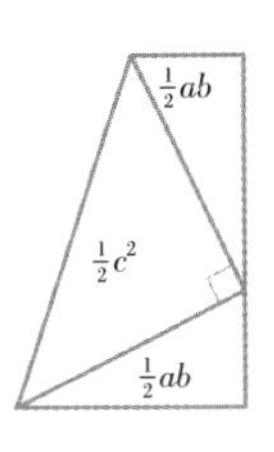

Garfield's Proof

For those of you who like your proof peppered with algebra, Garfield (the American president, not the cat) came up with a neat construction.

We start with two copies of a right-angled triangle. Position these to meet at a point with two sides in a straight line (which creates a right angle between the triangles–that the angles in a triangle add up to 180° can be used to prove this–see pp. 44–45). Join the gap to create a trapezium (as it is called in the UK, or a trapezoid as Garfield would have said). The area of the trapezium is the sum of the areas of the three triangles.

We can also find the area of the trapezium by a formula: the area is the average of the lengths of the top and bottom sides–$\frac{1}{2}(a + b)$–multiplied by the distance between these sides: $(a + b)$. These two expressions for the area must be equal.

$$\tfrac{1}{2}ab + \tfrac{1}{2}ab + \tfrac{1}{2}c^2 = \tfrac{1}{2}(a + b) \text{ x } (a + b)$$

Tidy up both sides:

$$ab + \tfrac{1}{2}c^2 = \tfrac{1}{2}(a^2 + 2ab + b^2)$$

Multiply both sides by 2:

$$2ab + c^2 = a^2 + 2ab + b^2$$

Subtract 2ab from each side, and so

$$c^2 = a^2 + b^2$$

Profile

Pythagoras

We can all recite Pythagoras' theorem: the square on the hypotenuse is equal to the sum of the squares on the other two sides. The theorem is part of popular culture, referred to by the Major General in *The Pirates of Penzance*, the Scarecrow in *The Wizard of Oz*, and Homer in *The Simpsons*. Pythagoras is part of our psyche.

Pythagoras was a Greek philosopher, mystic, and mathematician, living around the 5th century BCE, a charismatic leader who attracted a band of devoted disciples in a secret sect. Pythagoras believed that numbers had mystical and magical properties that you could meditate on and then experience ecstatic revelation.

His teaching was oral, and there are no contemporary written records of his work, possibly because of their secret nature. Our knowledge of Pythagoras comes from Cicero and various others, who wrote about his work several hundred years after his death.

• That Pythagoras' ideas live on is testimony to his argument that reason is immortal, all else mortal.

The Life of Pythagoras

Pythagoras was born in Samos in about 570 BCE, and lived till he was 75 or 80. He traveled widely, researching philosophical, mystical, and mathematical ideas in Egypt, Babylon, and possibly India. He settled in Croton and disseminated his religious and philosophical ideas, and lived an ascetic life. Pythagoras believed in metempsychosis, the reincarnation of the soul in animals, humans, and plants, again and again, until the soul achieved purity.

He and his followers formed an exclusive brotherhood with secret religious practices. This brotherhood was a kind of learning institution, which included women as well as men, and where property was shared. Members were bound by vows to the order. There were an inner circle of "learners" and an outer circle of "listeners." The learners had detailed access to the ideas of Pythagoras, whereas the listeners had summaries. They ate communally in groups of ten, and took part in daily exercises and musical activities. The painting by Raphael of The School of Athens gives a 16th-century vision of this brotherhood at work. The exclusivity of the brotherhood probably led to jealousies in Croton, and eventually Pythagoras had to flee. It is thought he died in Metapontum.

"There is geometry in the humming of the strings, there is music in the spacing of the spheres."

—*Pythagoras*

Pythagoras had an important influence on Plato, and so subsequently on future mathematicians and philosophers. There were three important influences. First, the Pythagorean brotherhood was a basis for the Platonic republic; second, mathematics was set as the logical foundation for science and philosophy; and third, the soul was an important idea as a mystical presence in the material world.

Pythagorean Tuning

The story is that Pythagoras passed a blacksmith's forge and he noticed the harmony of the beating anvils. He discovered that the sizes of the anvils were in proportion with each other, and that the harmonic intervals related to these proportions. He found that two anvils, one two-thirds the size of the other, will sound a fifth apart. If one is half the size of the other, they will sound an octave apart. Pythagoras recognized the simple arithmetical relationship involved in intervals of octaves, fifths, and fourths. Pythagorean tuning is based on the interval of the pure fifth. A pure fifth has a frequency ratio of exactly 3:2. Musical instruments work in the same way: a string that is half the length of another will sound an octave higher.

• A 15th-century illustration depicting Pythagoras' discovery of harmonic intervals.

THE BAUDHAYANA THEOREM?

Baudhayana was an Indian mathematician and priest who preceded Pythagoras by more than three centuries. He wrote the oldest of the four *Sulba Sutras*, which dates back to 800 BCE. They were texts that gave instructions to the Vedic people on how to construct religious altars. The rules of Vedic religious ceremonies were complex, and altars had to be built according to a specified shape, size, area, and orientation, depending on its religious purpose.

The Baudhayana *Sulba Sutra* records ways of constructing geometric shapes and preserving the area when transforming one shape to another. Baudhayana provided the first definition of Pythagoras' theorem, which is roughly translated as:

"A rope stretched along the length of a diagonal produces an area that the vertical and horizontal sides make together."

Perhaps we should call it the Baudhayana theorem, not the Pythagoras theorem.

THE GEOMETRY OF NUMBERS

Although Pythagoras' theorem is based in geometry, its biggest impact was on the world of numbers. A long-standing problem had been how to calculate the length of the diagonal of a square with unit sides. The Babylonians had calculated this to six decimal places, but the Pythagoreans knew that this was only an approximation. Try as they might, however, they could not find an exact value. Did such a number even exist? Pythagoras had the key for showing that it did, but it could not be expressed as a decimal.

Natural Numbers

The oldest evidence of early humankind counting is the Ishango bone, believed to be more than 20,000 years old. It has a series of notches carved along its length and is thought to have been used to keep a tally of something, although some scientists think that the way the notches are grouped shows that its creator must have had some understanding of calculating.

Whatever the actual use of the Ishango bone, the tallying up of one object in the world to one mathematical object (a notch) is the foundation of counting. We learn to count by saying numbers' names—one, two, three—in time with pointing to objects. So natural does learning to count seem to be that mathematicians call these counting numbers the "natural" numbers. Over time, mathematicians expanded this set of natural numbers. First, they created a number that was not in the real world (zero) and called this new set the whole numbers: 0, 1, 2, 3, 4, 5, and so on. Later this was expanded to include "negative" numbers. The positive and negative whole numbers together are called the integers.

The positive integers can be shown by counting out that number of beans or pebbles. But how do you show a negative integer? Marking the integers along a line became a powerful, metaphorical image for "showing" numbers, and, importantly, brings together geometry and arithmetic.

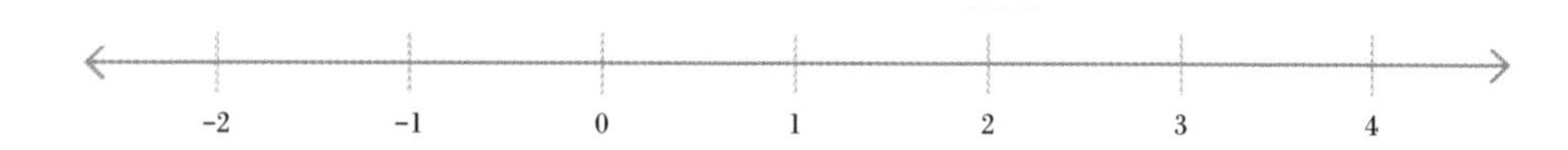

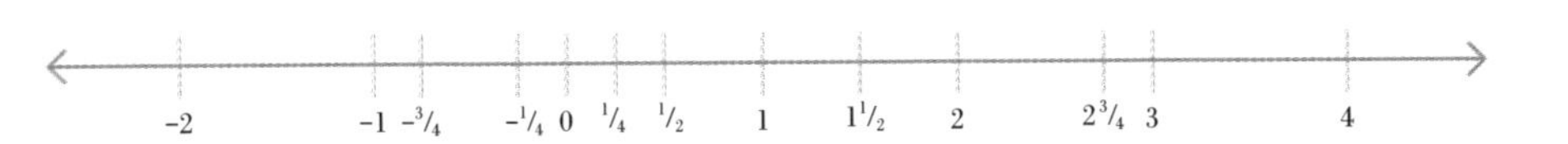

The set of integers served mathematicians well for a long time. They could answer calculations like 3 x 4, 53 + 7 and even 7 – 53. But while 12 ÷ 4 has an answer that is in the set of integers, 4 ÷ 12 rather irksomely does not. Not content to have calculations without answers, mathematicians created fractions to answer calculations that are impossible with only integers in your number toolkit ($\frac{4}{12}$ or $\frac{1}{3}$ in the case of 4 ÷ 12). Rather conveniently, the fractions, or rational numbers, can be marked on our number line.

While there are clear spaces between the integers on the number line—there is no integer between, say, 1 and 2—the rational numbers are very closely packed together. So closely packed that there doesn't seem to be any space between them. If you take any two, no matter how close together they are, you can always squeeze another one in between. Take, for example, $\frac{143}{560}$ and $\frac{144}{560}$. Close though these are, you can squeeze another rational number between them, such as $\frac{143.5}{560}$ (or $\frac{287}{1120}$ if you are unhappy with a fraction having a decimal number in it). This squeezing in can go on infinitely and, so it seems, intuitively. Were we ever to reach infinity, our number line would be solidly packed, with no room to squeeze in any more numbers. Or so logic would have us believe. Then along came Pythagoras and broke the logic wide open, as we shall see in the next section.

TRIANGULAR NUMBERS

Pythagoras studied triangular numbers as part of his mystical beliefs. The Tetractys is a triangular arrangement of points that add up to the perfect number—ten. The Pythagoreans worshipped the numbers one to ten and used the Tetractys for their mystical meditations. Prayers were even addressed to it.

• As well as symbolizing the four terrestrial elements—earth, fire, water, and air—the Tetractys also represented the organization of space and the cosmos.

NOT ALL MATHS IS RATIONAL

Mathematicians were happy that the number line of rationals was solid (see pp. 58–59) until along came Pythagoras, or his follower Hippasus to be precise. Legend has it that Hippasus was at sea with some fellow Pythagoreans and, with time on his hands, became curious about what Pythagoras' theorem reveals about the length of the hypotenuse on a right-angled triangle with the two sides of length 1. It had to exist but could not be expressed as a fraction.

Finding the Hypotenuse
With only our straight edge and compasses, we can construct such a triangle (see pp. 22–23)

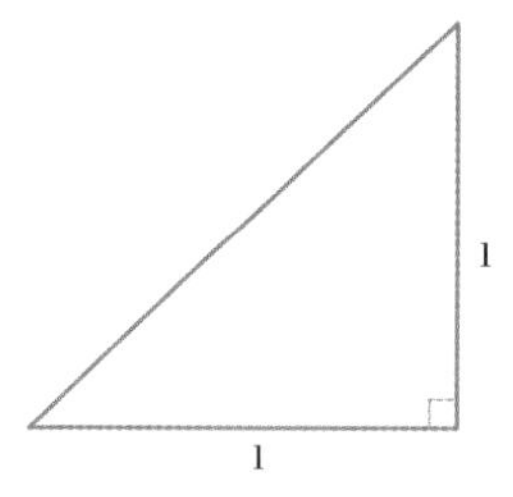

By Pythagoras' theorem, $h^2 = 1^2 + 1^2 = 2$. So $h = \sqrt{2}$. There is no doubt that this length $\sqrt{2}$ exists; it's there in the triangle. What piqued Hippasus' curiosity was how to express $\sqrt{2}$ as a rational number, a fraction. And that was his undoing. Let's look at the problem this presents.

We start off by supposing that $\sqrt{2}$ can be expressed as a fraction, say $\frac{a}{b}$. Any fraction can be reduced to its lowest terms; let's have $\frac{a}{b}$ expressed in its lowest terms, so that a and b have no common factors.

$$\sqrt{2} = \frac{a}{b}$$

Square both sides:

$$2 = \frac{a^2}{b^2}$$

Multiply both sides by b^2:

$$2b^2 = a^2$$

This tells us that a^2 is an even number (it is equal to 2 times b^2). You cannot square an odd number and get an even answer, so if a^2 is even, then a must also be even. We can write a as, say, $2c$.

Plugging $2c$ into our equation:

$$2b^2 = (2c)^2$$

or

$$2b^2 = 4c^2$$

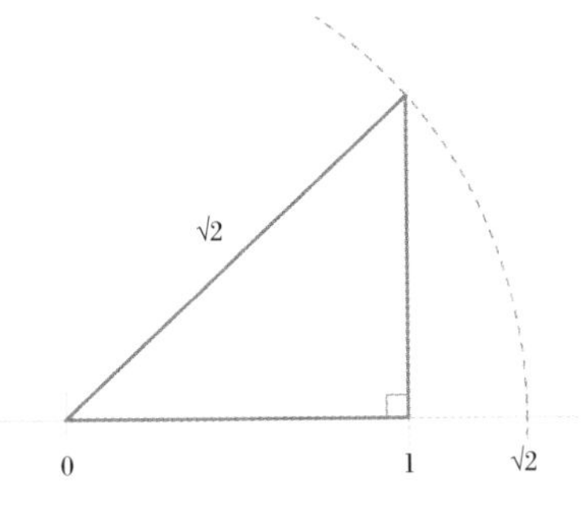

Divide both sides by 2:

$$b^2 = 2c^2$$

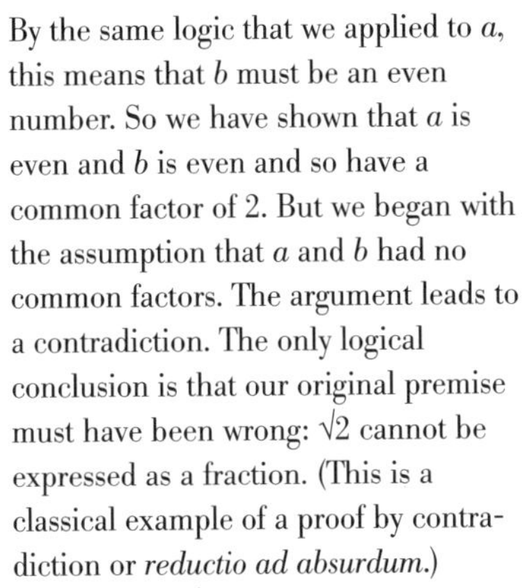

By the same logic that we applied to a, this means that b must be an even number. So we have shown that a is even and b is even and so have a common factor of 2. But we began with the assumption that a and b had no common factors. The argument leads to a contradiction. The only logical conclusion is that our original premise must have been wrong: $\sqrt{2}$ cannot be expressed as a fraction. (This is a classical example of a proof by contradiction or *reductio ad absurdum.*)

Although $\sqrt{2}$ cannot be expressed as a fraction, its position can be marked on our number line using our trusty compasses and straight edge. We set up our number line and position the triangle so that it sits neatly between zero and one. With our compasses, point on zero, we set the radius to be the length of the hypotenuse and draw the arc to mark $\sqrt{2}$ on the number line.

Rather than being packed solidly with the rational numbers, there is at least one gap on the number line where $\sqrt{2}$ has to fit. But it's worse than that. It turns out that there are an infinite number of numbers like $\sqrt{2}$ to fit on. Far from being solid, our number line of rational numbers has as many holes in it as an infinite string vest. All these missing numbers became known as the irrationals. Not because they are mad, but because they cannot be expressed as rational numbers.

Thanks to Hippasus' detective work, a whole new area of mathematics opened up without which modern mathematics would not exist. His reward? So upset were his fellow Pythagoreans at him unsettling their intuitions that they threw him overboard and he drowned.

Keeping It in Proportion

THE PROBLEM:

In order to save paper, Mike likes to reduce pages so that two pages reduced exactly fit into one piece of paper of the same size. What dimensions does his paper have to have for this to work?

THE METHOD:

Mike wants two pages reduced to exactly fit onto the same paper, which will need to be rotated through 90° for this to happen.

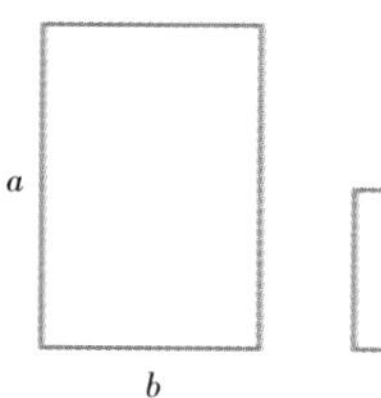

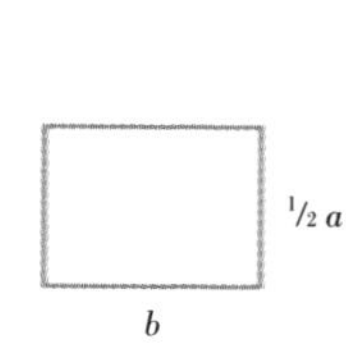

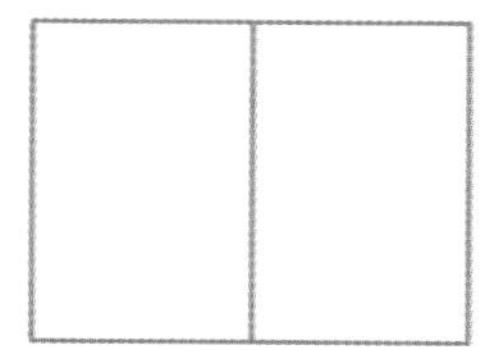

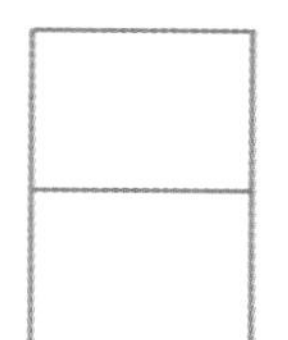

Mike needs to work out the ratio of the sides so that they are the same:

$$\frac{b}{a} = \frac{\frac{1}{2}a}{b}$$

(multiply both sides of the equation by b)

$$\frac{b^2}{a} = \tfrac{1}{2}\,a$$

(multiply both sides of the equation by a)

$$b^2 = \tfrac{1}{2}\,a^2$$

(multiply both sides of the equation by 2)

$$2b^2 = a^2$$

(take the square root of each side of the equation)

$$\sqrt{2}b = a$$

In other words, taking a sheet of paper and cutting it in half results in a smaller sheet that has exactly the same dimensions as the original. The height of the smaller piece is the width of the larger and the width of smaller is half the height of the larger.

There is our friend √2 again. Whatever length of side Mike chooses, if he makes the other side √2 times longer, his reduction will work.

In fact, Mike's work has already been done for him. The standard European paper sizes (A0, A1, A2, A3, A4, and so forth) are all constructed on this ratio.

A0 was constructed to have an area of 1 square meter, or 10,000 square centimeters. If the sides of A0 are a and $\sqrt{2}a$ centimeters long, then:

$$a \times \sqrt{2}a = 10{,}000$$

or

$$\sqrt{2}a^2 = 10{,}000$$

$$a^2 = \frac{10{,}000}{\sqrt{2}}$$

Which gives a value for a of around 84 cm and the other side of 119 cm (it is actually nearer to 841 millimeter by 1189 millimeter). All the other paper sizes follow from this. Format A1 is A0 cut into two equal pieces: the height of A1 is the width of A0, while the width of A1 is half the height of A0. AO reduces to A1, A1 to A2 and so forth.

THE SOLUTION:

Any sheet of paper where the sides are in the ratio of 1: √2 (about 1: 1.414) can be reduced (or enlarged) and maintain its proportions.

Professor Georg Christoph Lichtenberg, physics professor at the University of Göttingen, first proposed the ratio as a basis for paper formats in 1786, long before the advent of photocopying.

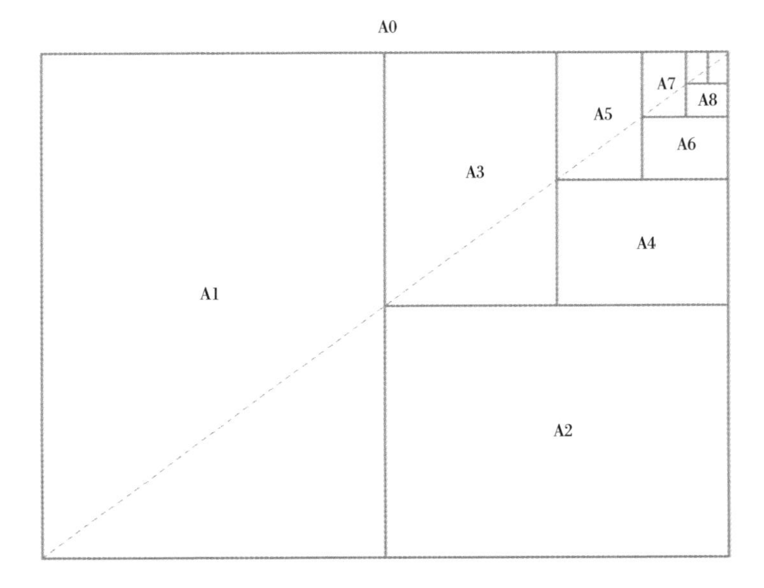

GOLDEN RATIO

Take a look at the rectangles below. Do any of them seem more esthetically pleasing than the others? Some believe that this is the case and the most pleasing "golden" rectangle lies behind much of our art and architecture. Mathematicians think they have the secret to the perfect rectangle.

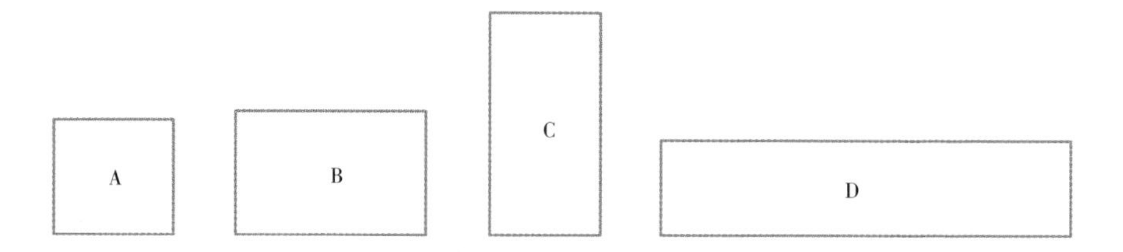

In Exercise #9, we encountered rectangles that, when cut in half, form two smaller rectangles of the same proportions as itself. We now move on to look at a slightly different problem.

We need to find the proportions of a rectangle that allows the following: when a square is cut from the end, the remaining shape is a smaller replica of the original rectangle.

• Cutting the square on the left from the paper produces a smaller rectangle with the same proportions as the original.

Since we are interested in the relationship between the lengths of the sides, rather than the actual lengths, we can choose simple lengths to start with, so let's take the length of the smaller side of the rectangle to be 1. We don't know the length of the longer side that we need, so call that length x.

If our original rectangle is 1 by x and we cut a square off it, then the dimensions of the rectangle left over will be $1 - x$ by 1. We want the ratio of the sides to be the same in each case:

$$\frac{1}{x} = \frac{(1 - x)}{1}$$

This is equivalent to

$$1 = x - x^2$$

(multiply both sides by x)

or $$x^2 = x - 1$$

The value of x that makes x^2 equal to $x - 1$ is approximately 1.618 (you can check this with a calculator—squaring 1.618 results in 2.618, just 1 more than 1.618).

This value is the "golden ratio," originally referred to as the *divina proportione* by the Italian mathematician Luca Pacioli in 1509. Building on Pacioli's work, Kepler described the golden rectangle as a "precious jewel." It is the ONLY rectangle from which we can cut a square and be left with a rectangle that is similar to the original one.

As well as establishing the ratio of the sides of a golden rectangle, the golden ratio can also be found on a line: it is the point dividing a line into two parts so that the ratio of the longer part to the whole line is equal to the ratio of the smaller part to the longer part.

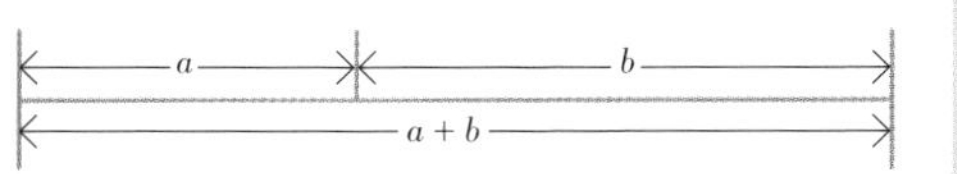

$$\frac{(a+b)}{b} = \frac{b}{a}$$

So important is the value of the golden ratio that it is given its own name and symbol: phi (Ø). The mathematical expression for Ø is:

$$Ø = \frac{(1+\sqrt{5})}{2}$$

FINDING THE GOLDEN RECTANGLE

Once Pacioli and Kepler drew the attention of the world's mathematicians to the golden ratio, claims for its existence abounded, even when they were perhaps not justified. The Parthenon in Athens is supposed to have been built on a golden rectangle, but the ratio of the breadth to height is not that close (1.74 as opposed to 1.618), and even then it depends on whether or not the pediment is included in the calculation.

Nevertheless, the golden ratio does seem to crop up a lot in nature, from seashells to the human ear. Each of these has a spiral construction: when an object grows in that form, the golden ratio is the most efficient means of scaling up providing maximum volume for minimum surface area.

• The golden ratio is not only nature's way of being efficient, it also produces beautiful objects.

Eye of the Beholder

THE PROBLEM:

Leonardo has heard about the beauty of the golden rectangle and wants to mark out his canvas with one. He also thinks that a triangular arrangement based on the golden ratio would be pleasing to the eyes, so wants to construct a triangle with this ratio built into it. He only has a straight edge and compasses to work with.

THE METHOD:

The proportions of a golden rectangle are formed in this way.

- Draw a square.
- Draw a line from the midpoint of one edge of the square to the opposite vertex.
- Use this line as the radius for a circle that touches two adjacent corners of the square.
- Extend the square with a rectangle so that the top edge of the rectangle is a tangent to the circle.
- The larger rectangle formed is in the proportion of a golden rectangle.

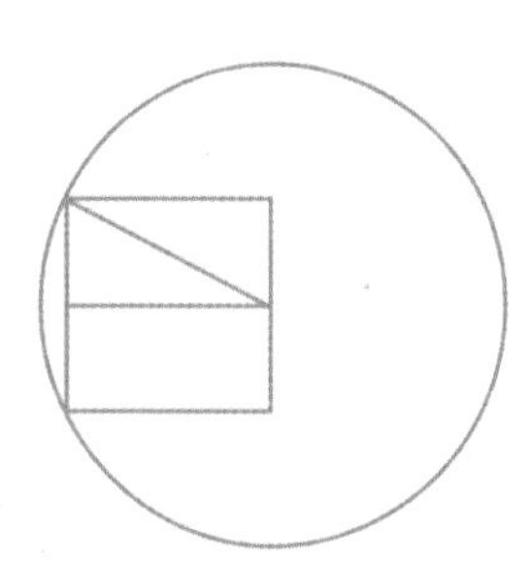
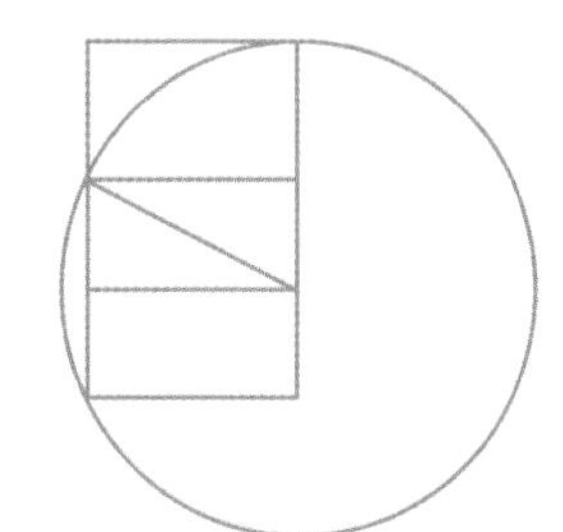

A pleasing triangle (known as "Kepler's triangle"), based on the golden ratio, can be constructed in this way:

- Use the length of the larger rectangle as a radius.
- Form a circle with that radius.
- Draw a radial line from the vertex of the golden rectangle to the arc of the larger circle.
- Kepler's triangle is the triangle formed by this line.

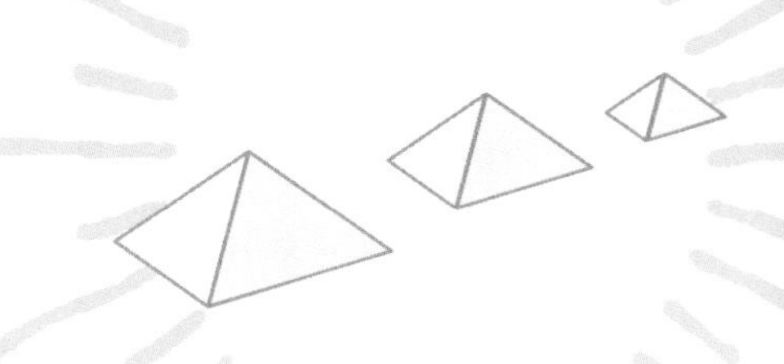

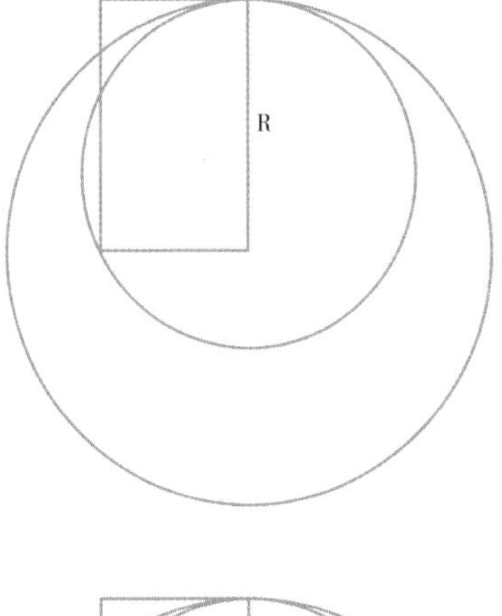

THE SOLUTION:

The triangle constructed in this way is known as a Kepler triangle. It combines two key mathematical concepts: Pythagoras' theorem and the golden ratio. Some think that the Great Pyramid of Giza has dimensions closely approximating a Kepler triangle.

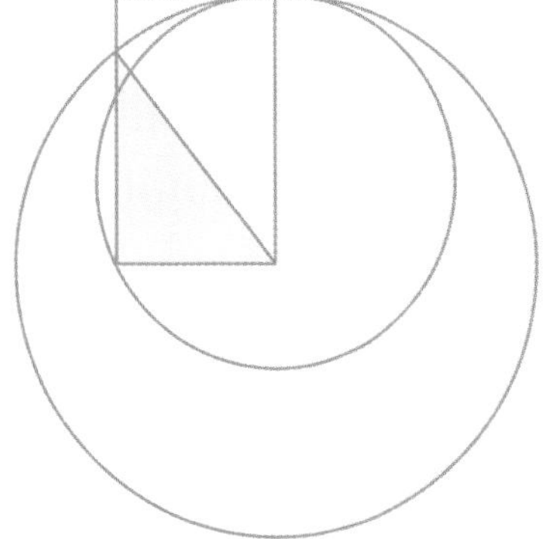

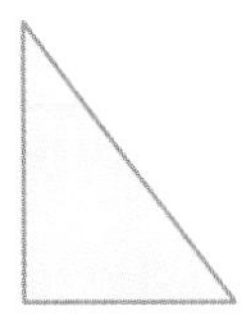

Exercise 11

Logarithmic Spiral

THE PROBLEM:

Felicity thinks the spiral that you find when you cut a nautilus shell in half is particularly pleasing. She wants to make a spiral path in her garden that is similar to the spiral in the shell. How does she construct this?

THE METHOD:

Felicity starts by marking out a square of sides equal to a length of 1 and then constructing a square next to it also with sides equal to length 1.

She then constructs a square above these two with sides equal to length 2.

Felicity continues constructing squares in a circular motion where each square has sides equal to the length of the sides of the previous two squares.

Felicity starts at the first square and draws an arc from one corner to the other, and then continues this arc in the same manner through all the squares. She ends up with the spiral she wants—a logarithmic spiral.

THE SOLUTION:

Felicity is constructing squares with sides whose lengths equal Fibonacci numbers (see p. 176). As Fibonacci numbers get bigger, the ratio of adjacent pairs gets closer to the golden ratio. The spiral is constructed in this way—the logarithmic spiral was also called the *spira mirabilis* ("miraculous spiral") by the mathematician Jacob Bernoulli. Bernoulli was particularly intrigued because as the size of the logarithmic spiral increases its shape stays the same. This is probably why the logarithmic spiral occurs so much in nature—because it fills space evenly and economically. This property of being "self-similar" is at the heart of fractals (see pp. 166–167).

• The construction of the logarithmic spiral mirrors the Fibonacci sequence insofar as the bigger it grows, the closer to the golden ratio it gets.

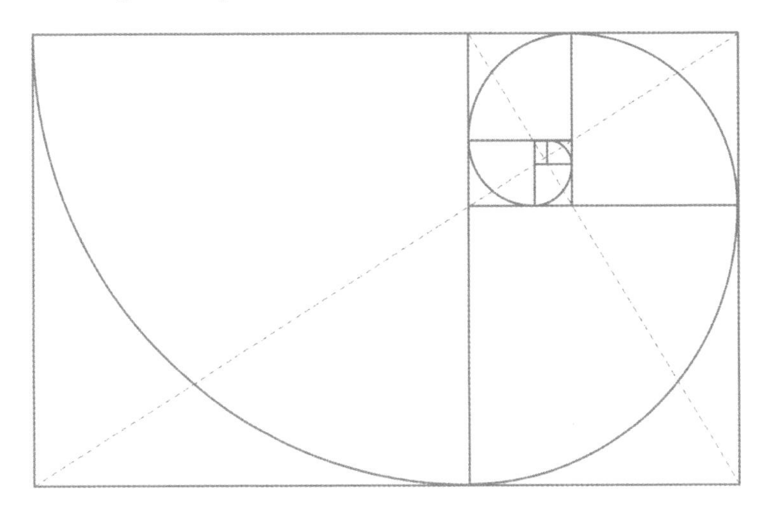

Profile Johannes Kepler

Kepler is remembered mostly for his three laws of planetary motion, but he made progress in many other areas of science and mathematics, including in optics, the discovery of two new polyhedra, theories on the packing of spheres, work on the golden ratio, and so on. Kepler's theories on geometry, astrology and cosmology, and his literary and rhetorical methods, are seen as central to the intellectual transformation from medieval thinking to the modern approach of the Enlightenment.

Dangerous Thinker

Kepler's logical and rhetorical methods influenced thinking in the 16th century. He rejected the non-scientific medieval approaches and led the intellectual transformation that became known as the Enlightenment. He worked on geometry, astrology, and cosmology, and we remember him mostly for his three laws of planetary motion. In geometry he worked on the golden ratio, discovered two new polyhedra, and developed theories about the packing of spheres.

Like Galileo and Descartes, Kepler subscribed to Copernicus' theory that Earth moves round the Sun—a dangerous view to hold in the 16th and 17th centuries. Like other Copernican thinkers of his time, Kepler suffered for his ideas.

The Life of Kepler

Johannes Kepler was born in 1571 near Stuttgart in Germany. His mother brought him up because his father, a mercenary, was killed in battle. His mother was a healer and herbalist who was later tried for witchcraft, probably because of Kepler's Copernican views. Kepler loved astronomy and when he was six his mother took him to see the Great Comet eclipse of 1577. In his higher education, Kepler was trained for the Lutheran ministry, but he excelled in mathematics and he took up a post teaching mathematics and astronomy at the University of Graz in Austria.

Kepler read the work of Copernicus, *De Revolutionibus*, published in 1543, and was convinced by the evidence presented in it that Earth revolved around the Sun. Kepler based his work on this theory. When he refused to convert to Catholicism he was expelled from his post at Graz, and from Austria, and because of his Copernican views he could not get work in Germany. Over the years he had corresponded with Tycho Brahe, the foremost astronomer and mathematician of the day. Tycho Brahe was not a Copernican, but he valued Kepler's detailed and precise astronomical observations, so he employed Kepler as his assistant in Prague.

On Brahe's death Kepler was appointed to the post of Imperial Mathematician to Emperor Rudolph II, in Prague, where he worked on his laws of planetary motion and developed his theories of the golden ratio. In 1610 he engaged in dialog with Galileo about the four satellites of

Jupiter. His beloved wife died in 1611, and in 1612 he moved to Linz, continuing work on astrology, and producing a catalog of stars and planets and their movements. He died in 1630.

Kepler's Published Works

Kepler's first major work, published in 1596, was on astrology, *Mysterium Cosmographicum* (*The Mysteries of the Universe*). In this book he described the Platonic solids. He devised a series of nested orbs, whereby each Platonic solid was inscribed and circumscribed by a sphere. He related these to the movement of the planets, seeing them as God's geometric plan for the universe.

In *Astronomia Nova* (*A New Astronomy*), published in 1609, Kepler detailed his first law of planetary motion: that all planets move in ellipses, with the Sun at one focus. He developed his theories of the golden rectangle, "a precious jewel." He wrote, "Geometry has two great treasures: one is the theorem of Pythagoras, and the other the division of a line into extreme and mean ratio; the first we may compare to a measure of gold, the second we may name a precious jewel."

• Nested Platonic solids.

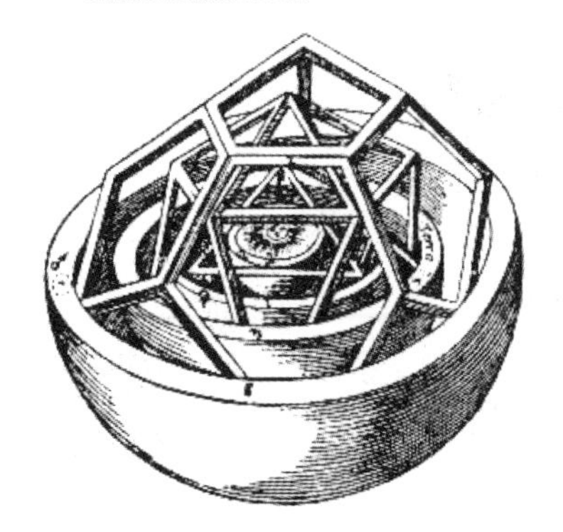

TYCHO BRAHE

Tycho Brahe (1546–1601) was a Danish astronomer and alchemist. He became the foremost astronomer in Europe, sponsored by rich patrons. Tycho was not a Copernican, but believed that the Sun and the Moon orbited Earth, while the other planets orbited the Sun. This was a favored theory of the Church. His detailed observations of the movement of stars were invaluable to Kepler.

In 1619 Kepler published *Harmonices Mundi* (*The Harmony of the Worlds*), in which he related the proportions of the natural world to music and explored the properties of regular polygons and regular solids. The *Rudolphine Tables* (named after Emperor Rudolph II), published in 1627, was prohibited in the period of the Catholic Counter-Reformation. It is a catalog of stars and planets and their movements.

Copernicus

Nicolaus Copernicus (1473–1543) was a Polish astronomer who first presented the idea that the planets revolve around the Sun, not Earth. He delayed publication of his book, *De Revolutionibus*, because of the dissension it would cause. It was published just before his death. First the Protestant then the Catholic Church denounced this "Pythagorean" theory, and the Catholic Church only removed the book from its proscribed list in 1835.

Profile Archimedes

Archimedes was an outstanding Greek engineer and physicist who invented machinery for everyday use as well as sophisticated weapons of war. One practical invention was what we now call the Archimedes Screw, a screw within a cylinder that allows water to travel upwards. We all know about his discovery, in his bath, of the principles of buoyancy, when he cried *eureka*! ("I have found it!") and ran through the streets of Syracuse proclaiming his discovery. He is also famous for discovering the principle of the lever, about which he said, "Give me a place to stand and I will move the Earth."

Although his inventions were considered at the time the most important focus of his work, he believed that mathematics was the only subject worth studying. He is thought to be one of the greatest mathematicians, but at the time, and for centuries after his death, his mathematical writings were largely not read.

The Life of Archimedes

Archimedes was born in 287 BCE in Syracuse on the east coast of Sicily, which was part of the Greek empire. He was educated in Alexandria in Egypt, probably with the successors of Euclid. He died in 212 BCE during the second Punic War, when the Romans captured Syracuse after a two-year siege. Rumor has it that he was killed by a Roman soldier because he was too preoccupied with mathematics to obey orders. The soldier had been told to take him unharmed, as a valuable asset, but Archimedes was drawing large circles in the sand with his mathematical instruments and reportedly said, "Do not disturb my circles."

We do not know much about the life of Archimedes—we only know about the works that survive, and what was written about him many years after his death. Plutarch wrote of him that he was so involved in thinking about geometry that he neglected to eat and drink and to look after himself, and that he had to be dragged to the baths to be washed.

The Archimedes Palimpsest

In 1906, unknown works by Archimedes were discovered in what is now called the Archimedes Palimpsest, an original manuscript that was overwritten with religious writings in the Middle Ages. Some of it was decipherable with careful scholarship, but it was not until the end of the

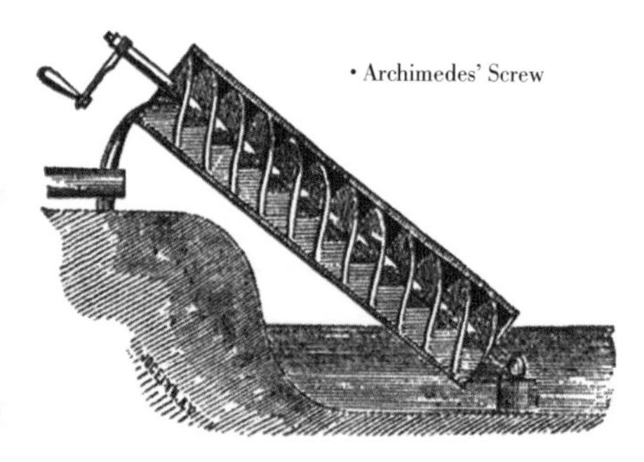

• Archimedes' Screw

20th century that it was fully accessible through digital processing. The most remarkable part of the manuscript is the only known record of Archimedes' method for finding areas of plane shapes, and surface areas and volumes of spheres, cones, and cylinders using the exhaustion method. This is an early form of integral calculus.

The Works of Archimedes

The works of Archimedes that have survived show him to be a polymath: *On Plane Equilibriums* explores mechanics using geometry; *The Quadrature of the Parabola* calculates the area of a segment of a parabola; *On the Sphere and Cylinder* looks at surface areas and volumes; *On Spirals* deals with the properties of spirals; *On Conoids and Spheroids* explores the moving and rotating of cones and spheres; *On Floating Bodies* covers hydrostatics; *Measurement of a Circle* attempts to define pi; and *The Sandreckoner* looks at number theory.

Method of Exhaustion

Archimedes proposed that the area of a circle could be calculated by finding the area of a triangle with the same height as the radius of the circle, and the base the same length as the circumference of the circle (see diagram below).

His proof for this was to take a circle and circumscribe and inscribe it with a square. This he divided equally with diagonals to make an octagon, then again to make a 16-sided figure, and so on.

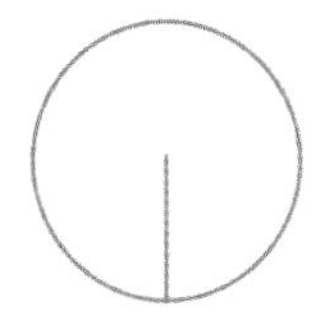

Each time, the circumscribed and inscribed polygons become nearer and nearer the shape of the circle. Each of the polygons is made up of triangles. You can find the area of one triangle in the polygon by calculating half of the product of the radius and the length of the edge of the polygon. To get the area of the circle, multiply the area of the triangle by the number of sides of the polygon. When the polygon has too many sides to count reasonably, a quicker way is to think of just one triangle with the height of the radius and all the sides of the polygon added together, which is, effectively, the circumference.

Archimedes proved that as the circumscribed and inscribed polygons get nearer to the circle, the difference between them becomes less, so that in the end the circle becomes a polygon with an infinite number of sides.

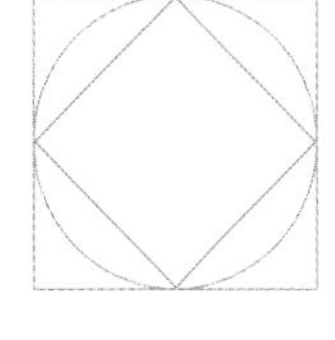

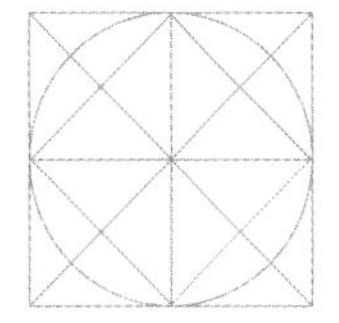

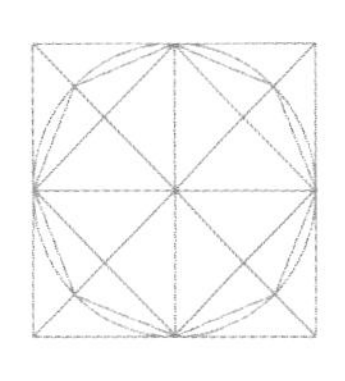

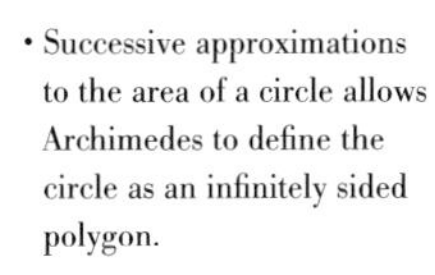

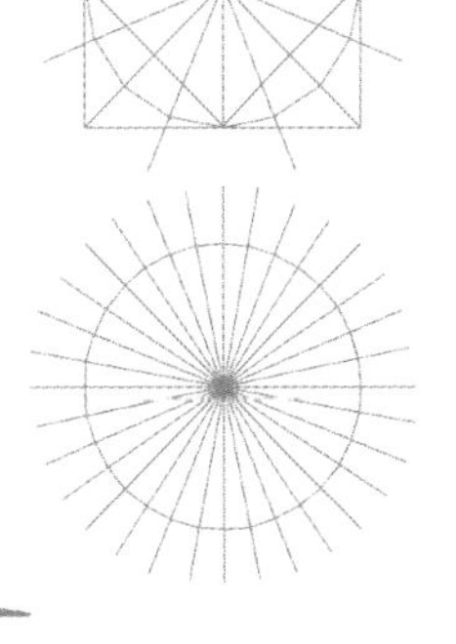

• **Successive approximations to the area of a circle allows Archimedes to define the circle as an infinitely sided polygon.**

Chapter

To Boldly Go

Much of Euclid's *Elements* dealt with two-dimensional space, but toward the end of these works his attention turned to examining two-dimensional space and in particular those solid shapes that are perfectly regular. But Euclid could never have imagined how, one day, mathematicians would be happy with the idea that the number of dimensions does not have to stop at three.

PLATONIC SOLIDS

We live in a three-dimensional (3D) world, so it is surprising that early geometers spent so little time studying this. Perhaps this was because of the difficulty of representing 3D objects in two dimensions (2D). With no cheap paper, the ancients often relied on sketches in the sand. But Euclid did end his *Elements* with a look at mathematically significant 3D shapes: the Platonic solids.

Regular Shapes

In Chapter 2 we looked at the challenges in constructing regular polygons (a regular polygon has equal angles and sides all the same length). Moving into three dimensions, a polyhedron (literally "many-faced") is regular if it meets two conditions:

- All the faces (the flat sides of a polyhedron) are the same regular polgyon.
- At every vertex (the point where a number of sides meet) the same number of faces meet.

The familiar cube is regular: it has six faces that are all squares and eight vertices where three faces meet. A square-based pyramid has lots of symmetries and in the everyday use of the word may be described as regular. It is not, however, mathematically regular because not all of its faces are the same: it has four triangular faces and one square face. A six-faced polyhedron can be made from six equilateral triangles

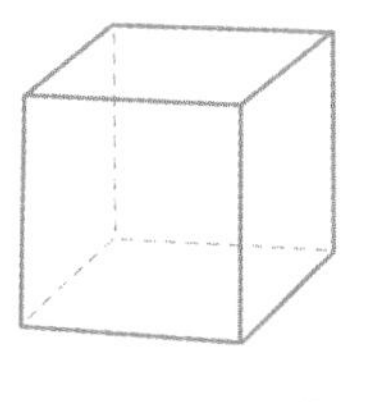

• Hexahedron (cube) has 8 vertices, 12 edges, and 6 faces.

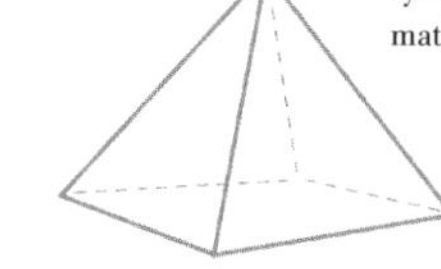

• A square-based pyramid might be called regular in the everyday sense of being symmetrical, but it is not mathematically regular.

but is not regular because at two of the vertices three triangles meet, while four triangles meet at the other three vertices.

In theory there are an infinite number of regular polygons. We can construct a 720-sided polygon with all the sides equal and all the internal angles equal, although unless it were very large it would look like a circle. Given that there are an infinite number of regular polygons to build from, can we also produce an infinite number of regular polyhedrons? Euclid established that the answer to this is no and that in fact there are precisely five regular polygons, which have become known as the Platonic solids.

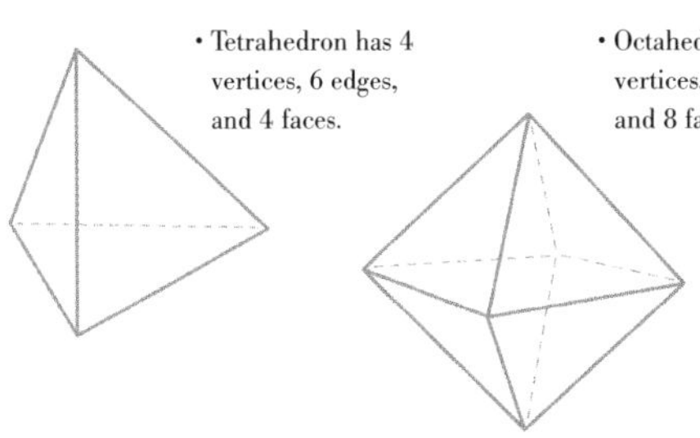

• Tetrahedron has 4 vertices, 6 edges, and 4 faces.

• Octahedron has 6 vertices, 12 edges, and 8 faces.

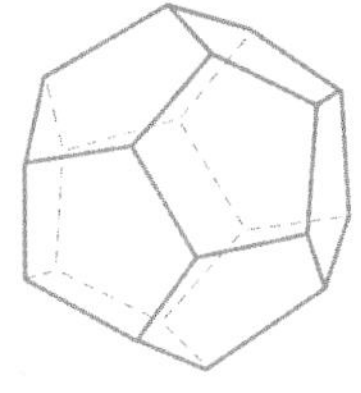

• Dodecahedron has 20 vertices, 30 edges, and 12 faces.

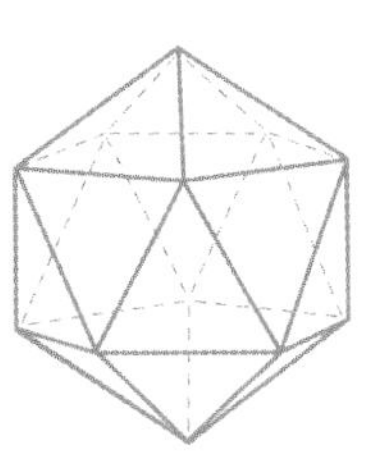

• Icosahedron has 12 vertices, 30 edges, and 20 faces.

The Five Platonic Solids

It turns out that there are only three regular polygons that can be used to construct a regular polyhedron. We have seen that six squares can build into a cube—the only Platonic solid with square faces. Equilateral triangles can actually be put together to create three different Platonic solids. Four equilateral triangles create the tetrahedron, eight the octahedron, and 20 the icosahedron.

The other regular polygon that can be used is the pentagon;12 of them create the dodecahedron.

The Pentagon

As we saw in Chapter 2, constructing triangles and squares with only compasses and a straight edge was simple for the Euclideans, but constructing a regular pentagon was an intractable problem. The pentagon has properties that fascinated Euclid. A pentagon with all the diagonals drawn in creates the pentagram, a five-pointed star.

A pentagon is special. Irrespective of the size of the pentagon, the ratio of the length of the diagonal of the pentagon to the length of the side is the golden ratio $\frac{(1 + \sqrt{5})}{2}$ (see pp. 64–65). So although Hippasus is generally credited with showing that some numbers were irrational through his study of the Pythagorean theorem, it also seems that Euclid, among others, had some sense of irrational numbers through their study of the Platonic solids. Some historians of mathematics suggest that it was the study of irrational numbers that really interested Euclid and that the Platonic solids simply provide a vehicle for this. The number theory that Euclid introduces in his study of regular solids is not actually needed to understand the solids themselves, so maybe he was trying to introduce irrational numbers by the back door.

THE PLATONIC SOLIDS AND THE ELEMENTS

The Pythagoreans associated the Platonic polyhedra with the four classic elements:

tetrahedron = earth
cube = water
octahedron = air
dodecahedron = fire

And the icosahedron? They associated this with "quintessence," which means, well, fifth element!

Profile

Plato

Plato is probably one of the greatest philosophers of all times. A. N. Whitehead, a mathematician and philosopher, wrote: "All of philosophy is but a footnote to Plato."

Plato wrote dialogues rather than philosophical treatises and in these dialogues Plato himself takes no part. He uses the Socratic method; that is, asking key questions to challenge thinking and promote deeper rational thought. The underlying principle is that each of us has to build up our own moral system from logical analysis and questioning of ideas such as "justice." Tempting and plausible ideas are put on trial—each idea must stand up to detailed scrutiny to be worthy of belief.

- Tradition has it that over the door to Plato's academy was inscribed, "Let no one ignorant of geometry enter."

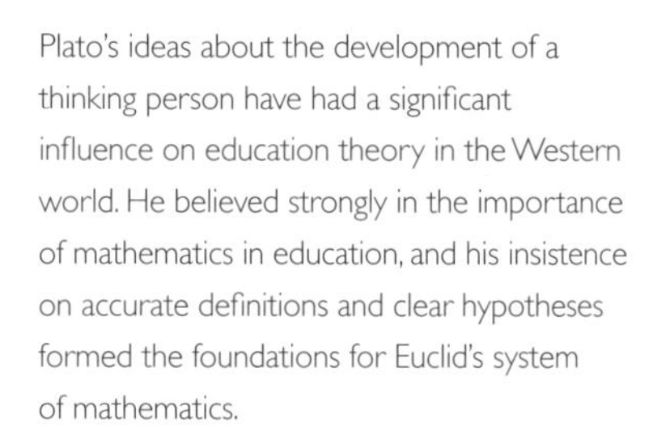

Plato's ideas about the development of a thinking person have had a significant influence on education theory in the Western world. He believed strongly in the importance of mathematics in education, and his insistence on accurate definitions and clear hypotheses formed the foundations for Euclid's system of mathematics.

The Life of Plato

Plato was born in Athens and lived from 428 BCE to 348 BCE. There is a legend that Plato, when he was a baby, was asleep one day when a bee settled on his lips and this augured the sweet words that Plato spoke during his life. He was nicknamed "Platon," meaning "broad," because of his broad shoulders and wrestler's build.

Plato's family was wealthy, influential, and political. Plato was initially interested in politics, but over time became disillusioned with the Athenian political classes. Plato met Socrates in around 409 BCE and he soon became a devoted follower. Socrates challenged his students to examine their ideas and beliefs critically, in particular ideas of justice and

"Then, my noble friend, geometry will draw the soul toward truth, and create the spirit of philosophy, and raise up that which is not unhappily allowed to fall down."

—*Plato,* The Republic

THE SOCRATIC METHOD

Plato employed what we now call the Socratic method in all his writings. The characteristics of Plato's Socratic dialogues are:

- They are not a lecture or an exposition, but a dialogue.
- The dialogue is between a teacher and a pupil.
- They are intended as a teaching tool.
- They are based on the use of irony, using the device of Devil's advocate.

The Socratic method involves using dialogue to find constantly improving hypotheses by painstakingly identifying and eliminating each one that leads to logical contradictions. A series of questions test logic and fact so that the learner can discover their belief about a topic. The aim of the Socratic method is for learning to be about how to think, not what to think.

goodness. This approach antagonized the Athenian rulers, who saw it as a criticism and a threat to the state. Socrates was executed in 399 BCE for corrupting the minds of the youth. Plato was greatly affected by this and after the execution he left Athens and traveled for 12 years with other friends of Socrates, visiting Egypt, Sicily, and Italy, and developing his philosophical and scientific ideas. He started writing the Socratic dialogues, based on the teachings of Socrates.

When he returned to Athens, Plato set up a college, which he named the "Academy" after the landowner, Academos—the name has been used ever since for the pursuit of learning. Many prominent intellectuals studied at the Academy, including Aristotle, who joined Plato at the age of 18 and stayed for 20 years until Plato's death. The Academy lasted for centuries until it was closed, as a threat to Christianity, in 529 CE. The Academy was a university of higher learning, for the study of philosophy, physical sciences, astronomy, and mathematics. In these first years Plato published what is called his middle works, including *The Republic*, a philosophical work on justice, courage, wisdom, and the role of the individual in society.

Plato became involved in the politics of Syracuse and was held a captive there for a number of years. He returned to Athens and the Academy and produced his late works, in which he used the Socratic method to discuss dance, music, poetry, architecture, drama, ethics, mathematics, politics, religion, and the philosophy of knowledge. One of these works was *Timaeus*, in which he wrote about what we now call the Platonic solids, and which formed the basis of Euclid's work. Plato spent the rest of his life teaching, debating, and writing, and died an old man at about 80 years of age.

Exercise 12

Painting Cubes

THE PROBLEM:

Maria is making a set of wooden cubes as building blocks for her daughter. She has six colors of paint and is going to paint each side of a cube in a single solid color. Maria wants each cube to have all six colors on it and she wants each cube to be different. How many cubes can she make?

THE METHOD:

Maria has the six colors—red, orange, yellow, green, blue, and purple—which we will represent by the letters *r*, *o*, *y*, *g*, *b*, and *p* respectively.

The first challenge here is to decide what is meant by different. Two cubes will be different if they cannot be rotated and positioned so that the arrangement of the colors on each is the same. In the nets on the following page, although they all look different, nets A and B when folded up to create a cube will have the colors in the same arrangement; net B will produce a different cube.

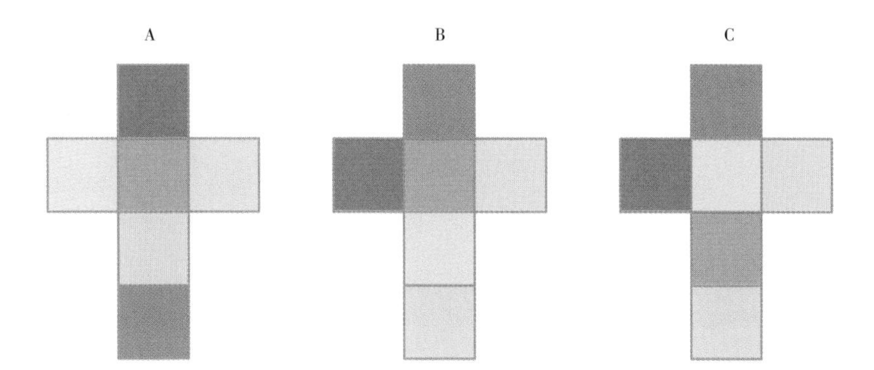

So how to keep track of the variations? Maria starts by thinking about one face as being the front and keeping that color fixed, as, say, red.

Thinking about the face opposite this red face, there are five remaining choices of color. Taking these one at a time, let us suppose orange is opposite red. The four remaining colors have to be arranged around the faces between the red and orange. There are six ways that this can be done:

ygbp

ygpb

ybgp

ybpg

ypgb

ypbg

Keeping red at the front and painting yellow on the opposite face, there are again going to be six different ways of painting the remaining four colors around the faces between red and yellow. The same holds true for green opposite red, then blue opposite and purple opposite.

There are five colors that can be opposite red, and for each of these five colors there are six ways of painting in the remaining four colors. Altogether there are therefore 5 x 6 = 30 different combinations.

THE SOLUTION:

Maria can create 30 different painted cubes. Just as she is about to start painting, she finds a tin of white paint and wonders how many cubes she can make with seven colors using six at a time for the painting.

Exercise 13

Largest Cube

THE PROBLEM:

Angelo is a box manufacturer. For years he has been stamping out nets of cubes from a square of paper that looks like this (ignoring any tabs needed to join the sides together):

One day he got to wondering if it was possible to start with the same-sized square of card and stamp out a net of a cube that when assembled would have a larger volume than the ones he had been making (and also waste less card). What is the largest volume cube that can be created by cutting out a net of a cube from a square of card?

THE METHOD:

We can choose the length of the side of the large square to be any figure that makes the working out easy, so let's start with a 20 x 20 square (the reason for this rather than, say 4 x 4 will become clear shortly). Each side of the original cube is 5 units long, so the volume of the cube is 5 x 5 x 5 = 125 cubic units.

Angelo thinks the cube will have a larger volume if he positions the net diagonally on the card.

• Angelo positions the net diagonally within the square.

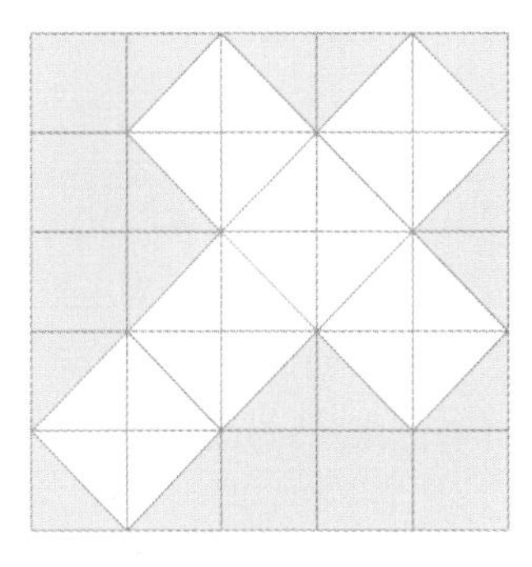

• With the grid marked out at intervals of four units, Angelo can calculate the volume of the resulting cube.

• Angelo's third attempt results in a volume almost three times greater than his first.

He needs to find the length of the sides of the squares on this net to figure out the volume. He marks off every four units on the large square (hence the choice of 20 units for the side).

Looking at this he can see that the side of each square in the net is the hypotenuse of a right-angled triangle with each of the other sides of length 4 units. So by using Pythagoras, the length of the side of the square must be the square root of 32 ($4^2 + 4^2$), which is about 5.66. Cubing this gives a volume of just over 181 cubic units. That's around a 45% gain on the previous volume.

Angelo went to bed happy that night, but woke with a flash of inspiration. He could make an even larger box.

The length of the side of a square in this grid is the square root of 50 ($5^2 + 5^2$), which is just over 7 and creates a cube with a volume of about 354 cubic units.

THE SOLUTION:

Angelo can create a cube from the same size square of card with a volume almost three times as large and waste much less card in the process.

ARCHIMEDEAN SOLIDS

Ask someone what shapes make up a modern-day soccer ball and they are likely to say hexagons. But you can tile a flat floor with hexagons, so how can they be stitched together to create a near sphere? In fact, a soccer ball is made up of hexagons and pentagons and is one of a collection of polyhedra, all of which are roughly ball-shaped, that intrigued Archimedes.

Truncated Cube

Imagine a cube made out of modeling clay that is solid all the way through. Now imagine slicing a piece off one of the vertices and so creating a new face. What shape will that face be? The slice will cut through the three squares that meet at the vertex and a triangle will be formed. If the cut is made accurately enough, then this triangle can be equilateral. Cutting the same size equilateral triangle off each of the eight vertices creates a new 14-sided polyhedron—which is basically a truncated cube.

The new solid has six octagonal faces (from the previously square faces) and eight triangular faces. Clearly this is not a regular (Platonic) solid as the faces are not all the same. But it does share some properties with the regular solids. Just as making the cuts in the right places can make all eight triangles equilateral, so too can the cuts be made so that the octagons are all regular. So while the truncated cube has two different polygons for its faces, they can all be regular. Also note that the new solid has 24 vertices (three where each of the previous eight vertices were); at each of these vertices there is always the same configuration of faces meeting—two octagons and one triangle. So there is a great deal of regularity to this polyhedron, and it's called, not surprisingly, semiregular.

Truncated Platonic Solids

As with the cube, we can create a semiregular polyhedron from each of the other four Platonic solids by slicing equal pieces off their vertices. If we examine the newly formed vertices, we find that, in each semipolyhedron, all the vertices are identical to one another. Because of this, we can describe each of these solids by noting which regular polygons meet at each vertex, in the order in which they are arranged. For example, we can define the truncated cube as 3, 8, 8—triangle, octagon, octagon.

Here are the truncated tetrahedron, octahedron, dodecahedron, and icosahedron. Can you match each up to its notation?

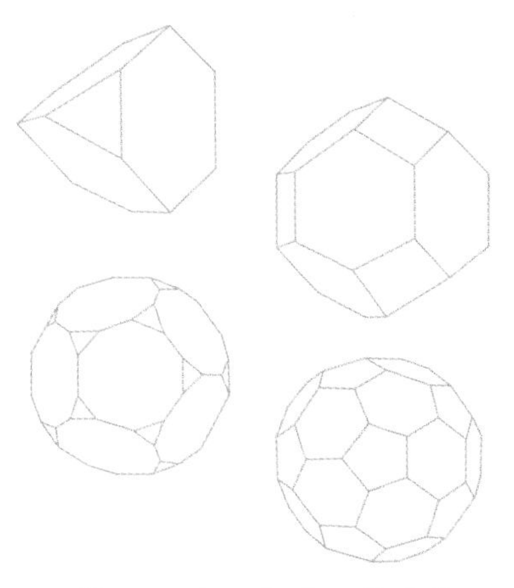

- Truncated octahedron (4, 6, 6)
- Truncated icosahedron (5, 6, 6)
- Truncated dodecahedron (3, 10, 10)
- Truncated tetrahedron (3, 6, 6)

If you are a soccer fan, you may have noticed that soccer balls are actually truncated icosahedra.

For anyone worried about inconsistency in the nomenclature, the cube does have another name—the hexahedron. So the truncated cube is also the truncated hexahedron.

Duals

Returning to our cube, imagine cutting larger and larger slices off the corners (and still slicing off equilateral triangles). At halfway along the sides of the cube the cuts will meet. While the truncated shape will still have 14 faces, the octagons will have become squares. The notation for this shape is (4, 3, 4, 3); at each vertex a square, triangle, square, and triangle meet in that order. This is the cuboctahedron.

A surprising result is that cutting midway along the sides of the octahedron creates exactly the same polyhedron. That is because the cube and octahedron are duals of each other. They have the same number of edges (12) and the number of faces on one is equal to the number of edges on the other and vice versa. The cube has six faces, the octahedron has six vertices; the octahedron has eight faces, the cube has eight vertices. If you imagine a dot in the middle of each face of a hollow cube and you treat these as vertices of a new shape, joining pairs of nearby dots creates a skeleton octahedron. And this works in reverse—dots in the middle of sides of an octahedron form the vertices of a cube. Hence the idea of one solid being the dual of the other.

The same is true of the dodecahedron and the icosahedron—they are duals of each other. Again, truncating either of these solids exactly midway along the edges produces the same semi-regular polyhedron: icosidodecahedron (3, 5, 3, 5)

So starting from the five Platonic solids and truncating them, seven new, semiregular solids can be created. Is that the complete set of semiregular polyhedra? No; it turns out that there are 13 such solids. These were defined by Archimedes and are named after him. A search on the internet will bring you images of the other six.

Euler's Theorem

THE PROBLEM:

Leonard was playing around with solid shapes and was intrigued by the idea that some shapes are duals of others (see p. 85). He pondered on whether this meant there was any relationship between the number of faces, edges, and vertices in a polyhedron. Systematically looking at the numbers of each of these on the Platonic solids reveals that there is a relationship.

THE METHOD:

The cube is probably the best place to start as we can usually find a die and physically count the number of vertices and edges. There are six faces, 12 edges and eight vertices and we can record this in a table.

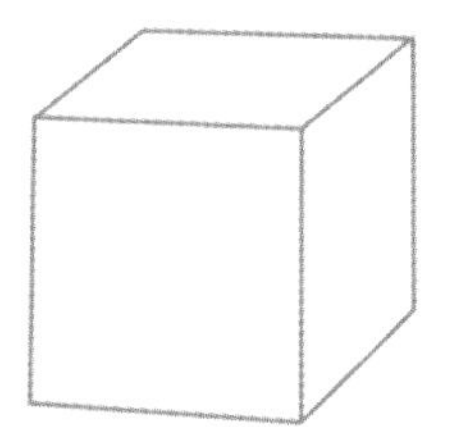

Solid	Faces (F)	Edges (E)	Vertices (V)
Cube	6	12	8

This table can be built up with the other Platonic solids.

Solid	Faces (F)	Edges (E)	Vertices (V)
Cube	6	12	8
Tetrahedron	4	6	4
Octahedron	8	12	6
Dodecahedron	12	30	20
Icosahedron	20	30	12

Before reading on, you might like to see if you can find a relationship between the numbers in the rows. Leonard reasoned that the fact that solids have a dual must mean that in any equation it must be possible to swap the values of F and V over and not mess things up. So the equation cannot have something like 2F + 5V in it, as 2V + 5F would not have the same value.

With a little tinkering with the numbers above you may have got the equation:

$$F - E + V = 2$$

This is known as Euler's theorem. You may like to test it out on some other solids. For example, does it hold true for a hexagon prism? Or a square-based pyramid?

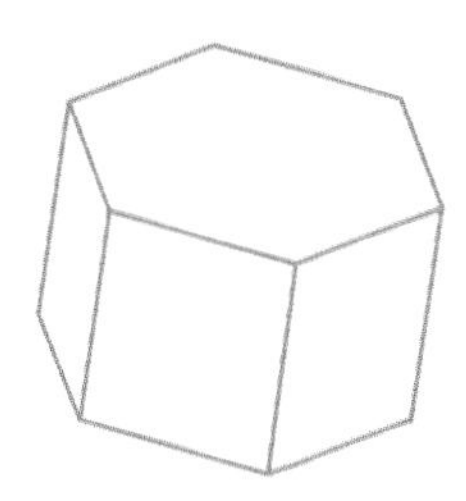

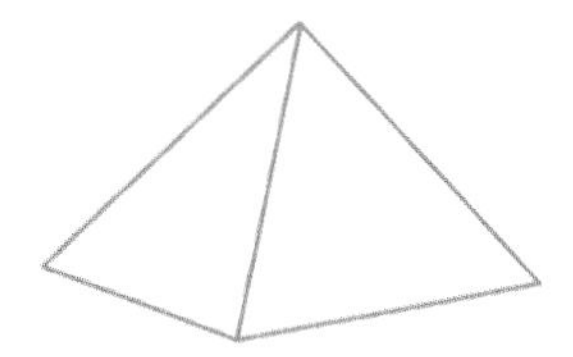

THE SOLUTION:

Euler's theorem shows that there is a relationship between the number of faces, vertices, and edges in solid shapes. However, it does not hold true in all possible cases. Check out a picture of a frame-type solid. If the front and back are not flat but recessed, then this solid has 16 faces, 16 vertices, and 32 edges. F − E + V in this case comes to zero. As we shall see later, solids with holes like this opened up many new problems for mathematicians.

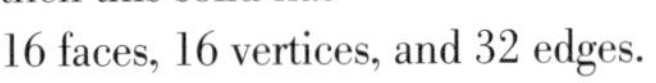

CARTESIAN COORDINATES

Maps are part of our everyday lives. We take for granted finding a location by specifying coordinates, whether in an A–Z of addresses or finding hidden treasure on an island in a pirate game. But the question of where objects are located in space did not occur to geometers until the 16th century. Euclid and his successors concentrated on the properties of shapes themselves. Then one day René Descartes got bored in bed.

Watching a Fly

Legend has it that, while lying in bed one day, Descartes watched a fly roam around overhead. He found that he could describe to himself each position of the fly by using just three numbers, and this way the inspiration for developing the Cartesian system of coordinates.

We first meet coordinates in two dimensions. Coordinates specify the position of a point (P) in the plane. Some other point is chosen and called the origin. Two lines are drawn through the origin, perpendicular to each other. These form the two axes and are conventionally labeled as the x- and y-axes. On paper these are presented as horizontal and vertical lines, for the sake of convenience rather than any mathematical necessity. The position of P is measured from the origin along the x-axis for a distance x, and along the y-axis for a distance y. To avoid confusion, these distances are conventionally recorded as (x, y), the distance along the x-axes from the origin followed by the distance along the y-axis. So (3, 1) and (1, 3) distinguish two different points (see above).

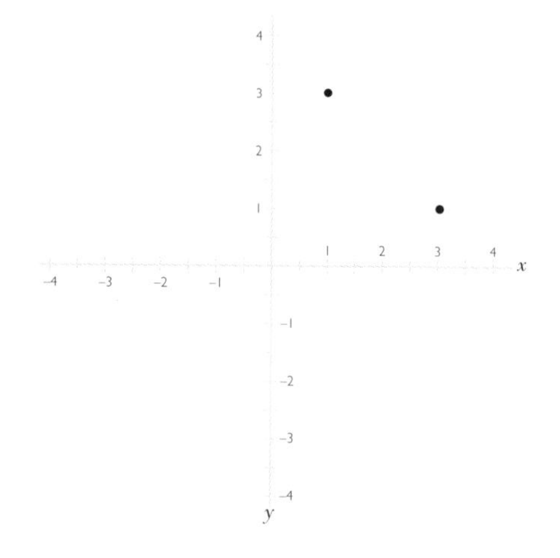

Three Dimensions

Descartes realized with his fly that anything not lying in the plane needs a third number to specify its location—how far above the plane it is. A third axis comes out of the plane at the origin, at right angles to both the x- and y-axes (and so cannot actually be represented on the page). Dubbed the z-axis, a point in space can be specified by (x, y, z).

The number of coordinates needed to specify a point gives us our language of dimensions. Flat, plane surfaces are called two-dimensional because we need two measures, two dimensions, to locate a point. Space thus becomes three-dimensional. If we just have a line and want to specify a point on that line, all we need is the distance of the point from the origin, hence lines are one-dimensional.

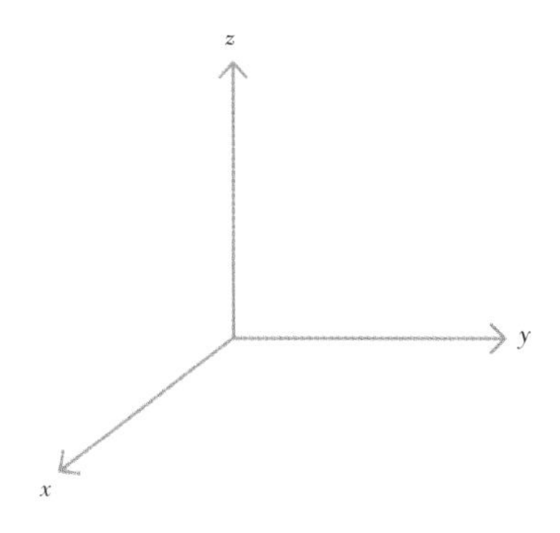

Far From a Footnote

Descartes first published his system of coordinates as an appendix—*La Géometrie*—to his book *Discourse on Method*. But the ramifications of his work changed mathematics forever. Now geometry and algebra were no longer distinct branches of mathematics. Geometrical forms could be expressed in algebraic terms, thus liberating geometry from relying on diagrams. Equally importantly, algebraic expressions could be given form and meaning through geometrical representations.

For example, in two-dimensional space, an equation involving x and y usually defines a line. For example, $x^2 + y^2 = 1$ means that the point (x, y) is always a distance of 1 unit from the origin. Extending this to three dimensions, equations with x, y and z create surfaces and $x^2 + y^2 + z^2 = 1$ traces out the surface of a sphere, its center at the origin and a radius of 1.

Fermat's Last Theorem

At the same time as Descartes was developing his coordinates, Fermat was studying the geometry of curves and developing his own coordinate system. Fermat used the idea of axes to create two coordinates (x, y). However, unlike Descartes, Fermat's chosen axes were oblique—that is, not necessarily at right angles. While Descartes is remembered for his coordinates, Fermat is more famous for this work on number theory and in particular his "last theorem." From Pythagoras we know that there are equations of the form $x^2 + y^2 = z^2$ that hold true for whole-number integer values of x, y, and z. For example, $3^2 + 4^2 = 5^2$ or $5^2 + 12^2 = 13^2$. Fermat's last theorem states that 2 is the highest power the three numbers can be raised to for there to be integer solutions to the equation. In other words, $x^n + y^n = z^n$ has no integer values when $n > 2$. Fermat did not prove this; it was left to Andrew Wiles to finally prove it in 1994. The proof relies on geometry and would not have been possible without Descartes' legacy of coordinates.

Exercise 15

Four-Dimensional Cubes

THE PROBLEM:

The writer H. G. Wells questioned why we had to restrict ourselves to only three dimensions. Why not extend geometry to four dimensions and beyond? We may not be able to construct a four-dimensional cube in the real world, but is it possible to create one in the world of mathematics? How do we describe a four-dimensional cube?

THE METHOD:

Cartesian coordinates allow us to specify the location of objects in space. Let's start with the humble square and assume it has sides of length 1. Positioning our square with one vertex at the origin of the coordinate axes, the positions of the four vertices are (0,0), (0,1), (1,0), and (1,1)

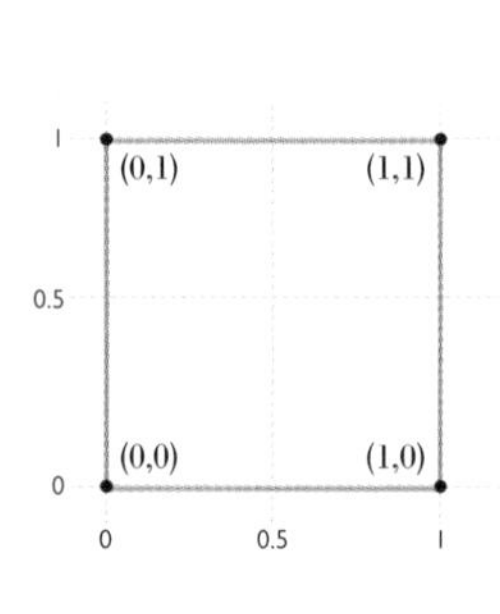

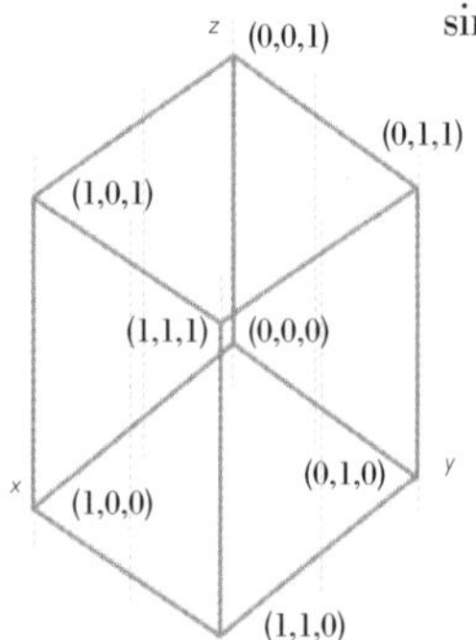

We can create a new axis—the z-axis—that comes "out of" the page at right angles to both the x- and y-axes. This forms a coordinate system where we can position the vertices of the cube.

We can also work back from our two-dimensional square to a one-dimensional line. We can plot any line on a single axis and we only need to specify the beginning and ends of the line. Our basic point on the line is at zero with coordinate (0); if our line is one unit long, the other point has coordinate (1). Now we can build up from the line to the square to the cube.

Dimension	Number of vertices	Coordinates
1	2	(0) (1)
2	4	(0,0) (0,1) (1,0) (1,1)
3	8	(0,0,0)
		(0,0,1)
		(0,1,0)
		(0,1,1)
		(1,0,0)
		(1,0,1)
		(1,1,0)
		(1,1,1)

We can see that the number of coordinates needed to specify a position is equal to the number of dimensions. A point in two-dimensional space needs two coordinates; a point in three dimensions needs three coordinates. As the dimensions increase, each existing coordinate is extended to provide an additional coordinate, taking the value 0 or 1. For example, moving from two dimensions to three, the coordinate (0, 0) is extended to create (0, 0, 0) (the same point in the x–y plane) and (0, 0, 1) (a new point created by the introduction of the z-axis). Hence the number of vertices doubles each time a new dimension is introduced.

Now there is nothing to stop us extending these into the fourth dimension. The number of vertices will be doubled to 16 and these can be generated by adding 0 or 1 as an extra coordinate to each of the coordinates of the cube in turn.

(0,0,0,0)
(0,0,0,1)
(0,0,1,0)
(0,0,1,1)
(0,1,0,0)
(0,1,0,1)
(0,1,1,0)
(0,1,1,1)
(1,0,0,0)
(1,0,0,1)
(1,0,1,0)
(1,0,1,1)
(1,1,0,0)
(1,1,0,1)
(1,1,1,0)
(1,1,1,1)

THE SOLUTION:

The hypothetical four-dimensional cube is known as a hypercube or tesseract. Although it cannot be constructed in the real world, we can create an image of its net.

Salvador Dalí used this in his painting *Christus Hypercubus*, which shows Christ being crucified on a tesseract.

COORDINATES ON A SPHERE

We have seen how the use of Cartesian coordinates allowed mathematicians to go beyond three dimensions and imagine a four-dimensional cube (see pp. 90–91). Coordinates permeate our lives now, from plotting the fluctuations in a patient's temperature over the course of a day, to getting the horizon level in a digital photograph. But such applications assume we are working in a flat plane. What happens when our surface is curved, like the globe?

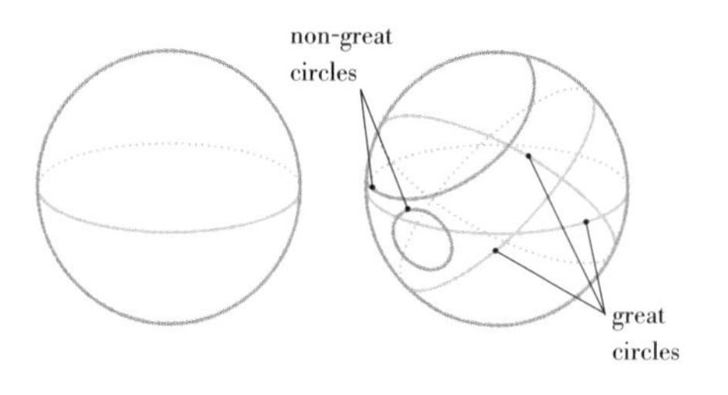

Locations on a Sphere

Plotting positions on a sphere—and for the purposes of mathematical modeling we will assume that our planet is a sphere—is still done using two coordinates. However, rather than specifying the distances along the x- and y-axes, the coordinates give readings of longitude and latitude.

Longitude measures how far round the curve of the globe you travel, east or west, from a given line of longitude, the prime meridian. Lines of longitude are "great circles," with the center of the Earth as the center of the circle.

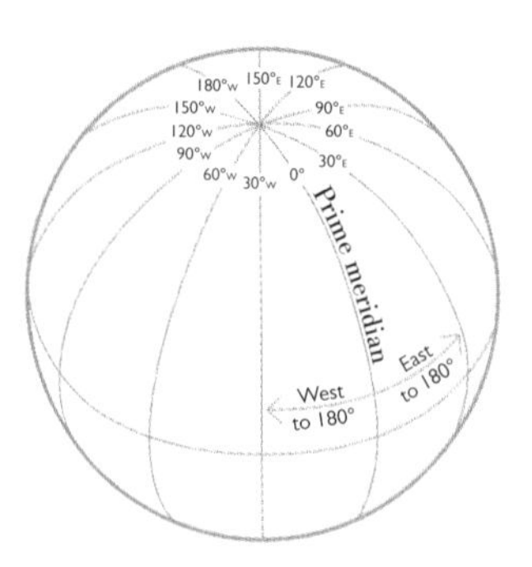

Every great circle on a sphere divides the sphere into two equal parts, two hemispheres. Any two points on the surface of a sphere have just one great circle joining them. You can imagine this by picturing a plane slicing through the two points and the center of the sphere.

Lines of latitude are also circles that go round the globe, but only one of these is a great circle—the equator. This great circle provides the base line from which movement north or south is calculated. Early navigators calculated their position according to the angle of the Sun above the horizon as it changed in line with the latitude. The navigators could measure this angle using a sextant and then calculate their latitude.

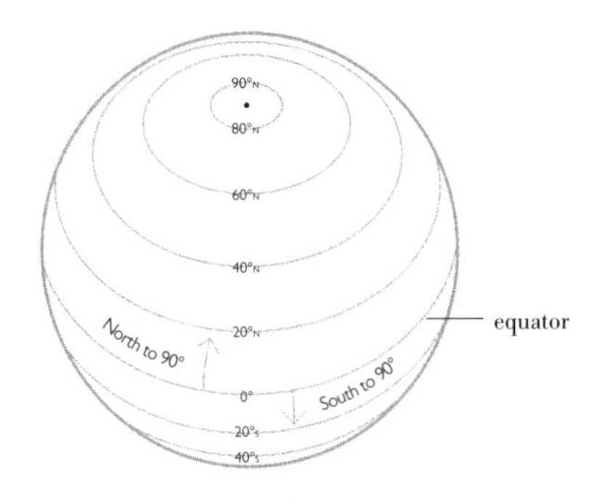

• Latitude measures the angle from the ground to the Sun at equinox.

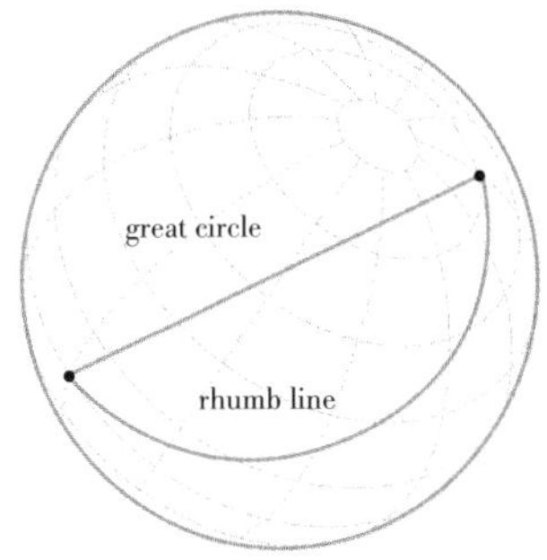

• The rhumb line plots a course based on a fixed compass bearing.

Working out the longitude is not so simple, and this stumped mathematicians and navigators for a long time. The study of sunrise and sunset and the movement of the stars and Moon finally solved the problem. By setting a very accurate clock to local time when setting out to sail, and comparing this time to local time on the journey enabled the calculation of longitude. In 1736, John Harrison invented a marine chronometer that solved the problem of calculating longitude accurately. Before then, shipwrecks and hundreds of lost sailors' lives were part of the risks of sailing the seas. Of course, sextants and accurate clocks have now been made redundant through GPS.

Rhumb Line

If you set out to travel between two points on a globe and traveled along the great circle joining those two points, then, in theory, if you continued to travel in the same direction, you would eventually end up back where you started. Now suppose that your map shows that your destination is due east of your starting point (and you are in the northern hemisphere and not on the equator). If you set your compass bearing due east and follow that line of latitude then you will not actually be on a great circle. The journey you take following a fixed compass bearing is known as a rhumb line.

Unlike following a great circle, continuing on a rhumb line will not bring you back to where you started but to one of the poles instead. That's because you would be traveling in a spiral, as the view looking down on the North Pole (below) shows.

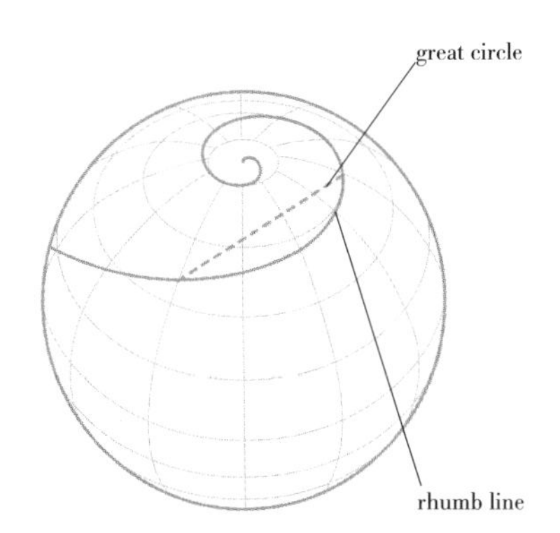

Flight Path

THE PROBLEM:

Settling down with a gin and tonic on a flight from New York to Rome, Sheila turns on the flight path map on the entertainment center. To her surprise, the plane does not seem to be taking the most direct route. Looking at the map in the in-flight magazine, she expects the plane to be flying almost due east. But the flight path map suggests it is going in a northerly direction. Is that correct, or has the pilot fallen asleep?

THE METHOD:

To explore what's happening here, let's create a simpler model. Suppose the radius of the Earth is 1 unit (we can scale this up later). Assume a simple journey that starts at a latitude of 45° N then travels to the point on the globe on the same latitude but 180° round.

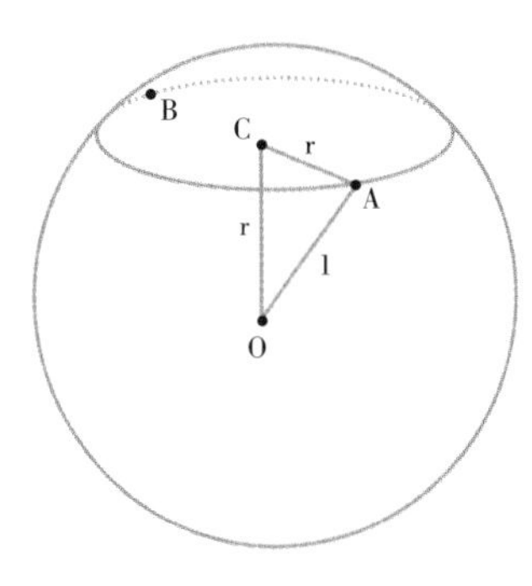

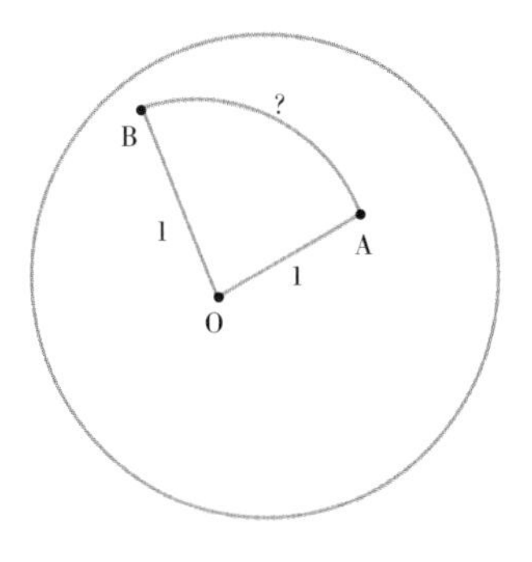

Traveling due east (or west), the distance we travel will be half the circumference of the circle with center C. We can find the radius, r, of this circle by applying Pythagoras to the ΔOAC, where O is the center of the globe. This triangle is isosceles since $\angle COA = \angle OAC = 45°$. Hence:

$$r^2 + r^2 = 1^2$$
$$2r^2 = 1$$
$$r = \frac{1}{\sqrt{2}}$$

The circumference of this circle is $2\pi r$, so half the circumference is $\frac{\pi}{\sqrt{2}}$.
The other route to explore between A and B is the great circle passing through A and B. This journey follows the arc AB on the great circle; since this arc creates a right angle at the center of the great circle the distance will be a quarter of the circumference of the great circle.

The radius of the great circle is 1, so its circumference is 2π and a quarter of this is $\frac{\pi}{2}$. Now $\sqrt{2} < 2$, so $\frac{\pi}{\sqrt{2}} > \frac{\pi}{2}$ (dividing by the smaller number gives the larger answer).

So in this particular case, it is shorter to fly on a path following a great circle than it is to fly due east.

This result holds true for any pair of points on the same latitude—the distance around the great circle joining them is always shorter than the distance joining them on the line of latitude (unless the points happen to be on the equator, which is a great circle). In fact for any pair of points on the globe, the great circle joining the points is the shortest distance.

THE SOLUTION:

The pilot is following the great circle joining New York and Rome, as this is the shortest distance. Sheila can sit back and enjoy another drink knowing the pilot will get her there as soon as possible.

Profile Johann Gauss

Johann Gauss was a German mathematician and scientist. He called mathematics "the queen of sciences," and he is known as *princeps mathematicorum*, the "prince of mathematics." He furthered a remarkable number of ideas in science and mathematics, including geometry.

Gauss realized the limitations of Euclidean geometry and he developed a new geometry for curved and multi-dimensional surfaces. He realized that the surface of Earth has parallel lines that can cross one another, for example, the lines of latitude are parallel at the equator and cross at the poles.

Prodigious Feats

Gauss was a child prodigy—he is listed in the top ten prodigies of all time. By the time he was three he had taught himself to read and to do complex arithmetic, and at this age he corrected his father's calculations on a complex payroll list. When he was a young boy, his schoolteacher gave the pupils the task of adding all the integers 1 to 100—in a few moments, Gauss had written the answer 5050 on his slate, having seen instantly the formula for the sum of an arithmetic series. He developed a remarkable facility for mental calculations, using a system of mental logarithms. When he was 19, Gauss worked out how to construct a 17-sided polygon with Euclid's tools—compasses and a straight edge. He had discovered what geometers since Euclid had been unable to do.

After his death, his brain was removed from his skull and measured. It was large and heavy, and had unusual deep crevices. It was thought for years that this was the sign of a genius.

The Life of Gauss

Johann Carl Friedrich Gauss (pictured, left, in a lithograph from 1828) was born in 1777 in Brunswick, Germany. His parents were poor and uneducated, and his father was a stonemason. Gauss went to the local school where he excelled, and he came to attention of the Duke of Brunswick, who sponsored his education at college and university. At each of these academies, Gauss made several important mathematical discoveries.

In 1801, when he was 24, he published *Disquisitiones Arithmeticae*. During this year, Gauss calculated the position of the lost planet Ceres, inventing a statistical process of normal distribution, also called the Gaussian distribution, for predicting its course.

After the death of his benefactor in 1807, Gauss was appointed director of a new observatory in Göttingen. In 1818 he invented the heliotrope, an instrument using a mirror to

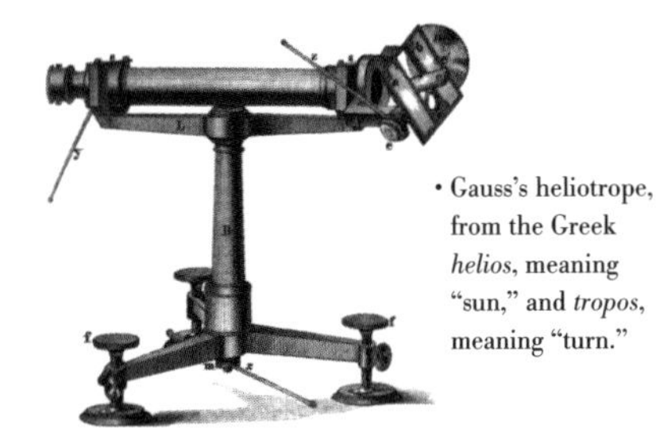

• Gauss's heliotrope, from the Greek *helios*, meaning "sun," and *tropos*, meaning "turn."

reflect sunlight over great distances, which he used for undertaking a geodesic survey of the state of Hanover. This led to his theories of non-Euclidean geometry, which he did not publish because he did not want to trigger arguments with entrenched Euclideans. When two other mathematicians—his student János Bolyai and the Russian Nikolai Lobachevsky—subsequently published non-Euclidean theories, Gauss claimed that these were his ideas.

Gauss worked at the observatory on a range of scientific and mathematical ideas. He would not publish less than perfect works and hence he published relatively little in his lifetime. He married twice and had seven children. It is said that he was interrupted while in the middle of working on a problem to be told that his wife was dying. He said, "Tell her to wait a moment till I'm done." He died in Göttingen in 1855.

THINGS NAMED AFTER GAUSS

Gauss's name is used for an astonishing range of things and ideas, showing the profound influence he had on mathematics and science. Here are just a few examples:

- Gauss's Law, used in physics in electrostatics.
- The gauss, G, is the unit of measurement of a magnetic field: the Earth's magnetic field is 0.31–0.58 gauss.
- Degaussing, a method of demagnetizing an object.
- The Gauss map provides a mapping from every point on a curve or a surface to a corresponding point on a unit sphere.
- Gaussian curvature is the measure of curvature of a surface.
- The Gauss expedition was the maiden German South Polar voyage of the ship the *Gauss* in 1901–3, during which an extinct volcano was named Gaussberg.
- The asteroid Gaussia.
- The Gauss Tower, an observation tower in Germany.
- The Gauss crater on the Moon.
- The Gaussian distribution is the normal curve, or bell curve, in statistics.
- A Gaussian integer is a complex number whose real and imaginary parts are both integers.
- Gauss's Constant is defined as the reciprocal of the arithmetic-geometric mean of 1 and the square root of 2.
- Gauss computer software that displays lines and surfaces defined algebraically in 3D.

Going on a Bear Hunt

THE PROBLEM:

Christopher is on a bear hunt. He leaves his tent and walks dues south in a straight line for 30 minutes, and then he turns left through a right angle. He walks for another 30 minutes, again in a straight line, and then turns left again through another right angle. After another 30 minutes walking in a straight line he is back at his tent. All the while a bear has been watching him. What color is the bear?

THE METHOD:

The bear has to be white. To follow these instructions, Christopher has to be at the North Pole. But something is odd here. Christopher walks in three straight lines and ends up back where he started. So he must have walked along the three sides of a triangle. But he also made two 90° turns. How can that be? The angles of a triangle add up to 180°. No triangle can contain two right angles. What is going on?

We start by looking at the argument for why the angles of a triangle add up to 180°. We draw a triangle ABC with base AB and a line parallel to the base passing through C.

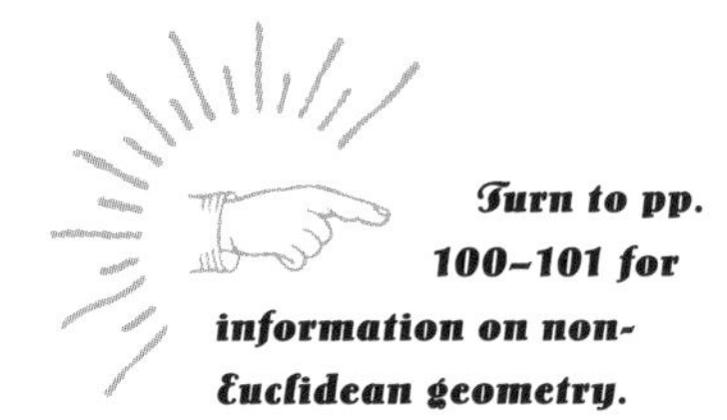
Turn to pp. 100–101 for information on non-Euclidean geometry.

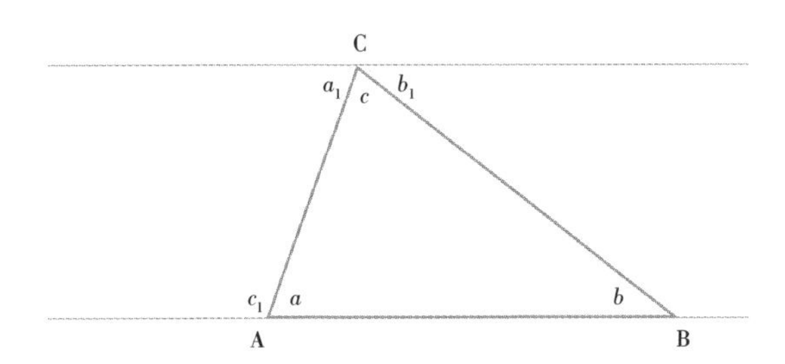

Because of the two parallel lines, angles a and a_1 are equal and so are angles b and b_1, a_1, b_1, and c_1 all form a straight line and so add up to 180°. Therefore $a + b + c = 180°$.

But this reasoning only holds for a flat triangle; strange things happen on a sphere. Forgetting Christopher for the moment, imagine that the base of the triangle AB is sitting along the equator. We can still draw what looks like the same type of triangle. Its base is sitting on a great circle (see p. 92), but the line through C parallel to this is a line of latitude and NOT a great circle. The result of this is that angle a is actually bigger than a_1 and b is also larger than c_1. So although a_1, b_1 and c_1 still add up to 180°, a, b, and c actually total more than that.

THE SOLUTION:

Triangles in a flat plane do have angles that add up to 180°. But triangles drawn on the surface of a sphere can have angles that total to more than 180°. This observation challenged Euclid's rule over geometry and opened up the way to other, non-Euclidean, geometries.

Profile

Nikolai Lobachevsky

Lobachevsky was a Russian mathematician, sometimes called the Copernicus of geometry. In 1829, he published a paper outlining a non-Euclidean geometry where Euclid's fifth postulate no longer held. Euclid's postulate stated that given a line and a point, you could draw only one line through the point that is parallel to the first line. Lobachevsky developed a geometry for curved surfaces where parallel lines, meet and diverge. A Hungarian mathematician, János Bolyai, also developed non-Euclidean geometry simultaneously. Lobachevsky and Bolyai did not know each other.

Lobachevsky's big idea was to imagine that there could be more than one possible way to construct a line through a point that will not intersect with another line positioned parallel to it. The exciting consequence of this was that the sum of angles in a triangle need not be 180°.

Actually, Gauss had developed these theories himself 30 years previously, but had failed to publish them. Gauss claimed that his work had influenced both Lobachevsky and Bolyai. This accusation was made famous by the American mathematician and satirist Tom Lehrer in his song, "Lobachevsky."

When János Bolyai discovered that Lobachevsky had published his discovery first, he became convinced that Gauss had invented the character "Lobachevsky" in order to deprive Bolyai of the honor of the discovery.

"I will never forget the day I first met the great Lobachevsky. In one word he told me the secret of success in mathematics: Plagiarize!"—*Tom Lehrer*

The Life of Lobachevsky

Nikolai Ivanovich Lobachevsky (1792–1856) was educated at Kazan University, where a former teacher of Gauss taught him. He became a professor at the same university, teaching mathematics, physics, and astronomy. He married and had 15 children, although only three of them survived childhood. His health deteriorated, and he left the university in 1846. He died in poverty in 1856.

Scandalous Work?

Lobachevsky's main achievement was in non-Euclidean geometry. He lectured on the subject and in 1829 published the paper "A concise outline of the foundations of geometry," followed by "New foundations of geometry" in 1835. Gauss had expected these ideas to cause a scandal, which is why he himself did not publish them 30 years earlier. But Lobachevsky's papers did not make an impact, which disappointed Lobachevsky. Actually, the ideas were indeed revolutionary, and had a profound influence on geometry subsequently.

Profile

William Hamilton

William Rowan Hamilton (1805–1865), was an Irish mathematician, physicist and astronomer who made important contributions to both mechanics and algebra. He was a child prodigy and by the age of five he knew Latin, Greek, and Hebrew. At 21 he was made Professor of Astronomy at Trinity College, Dublin, and Royal Astronomer of Ireland.

The Fourth Dimension

In 1843, on a walk with his wife, the idea of "quaternions" came into his mind. As the formula formed in his mind, he carved it on the stone of Brougham Bridge. He recorded, "And here there dawned on me the notion that we must admit, in some sense, a fourth dimension of space for the purpose of calculating with triples."

The belief that geometry must describe the real world meant that the idea of a fourth dimension seemed impossible. Once geometry was expressed in algebraic terms, with the acceptance of the square root of minus one, more complex ideas were possible. Gauss worked out how to interpret complex numbers as points in a plane. Hamilton continued the work, using just algebra. He struggled for years with the idea of a three-dimensional algebra, but found instead a four-dimensional algebra, which he called quaternions. Quaternions represent a number system that extends the complex numbers into four dimensions. They are now recognized as one of the most important concepts in modern computer graphics, offering a way to represent rotations.

HAMILTON'S GAME

In 1857 W. R. Hamilton invented a game. The object of the game is to travel along the edges of a dodecahedron so that you visit each vertex just once and travel along each edge just once, and end up at your starting point. The game was manufactured and sold commercially throughout Europe, using numbered pegs and a pegboard with holes at the vertices of a dodecahedral graph. Hamilton sold the rights to the game for £25. Called A Voyage Around the World, there was a flat parlor game and a traveling version with an actual dodecahedron. The game was not a success because it was easy to solve by trial and error, whereas Hamilton insisted on calculating the solution with his algebraic formula.

A path such as this, visiting every vertex and every edge just once and returning to the starting point, became known as a Hamilton circuit. Hamilton invented an algebra he called icosian calculus, based on the symmetry of the icosahedron. All Platonic solids can be graphed on a flat plane and each has a Hamilton circuit.

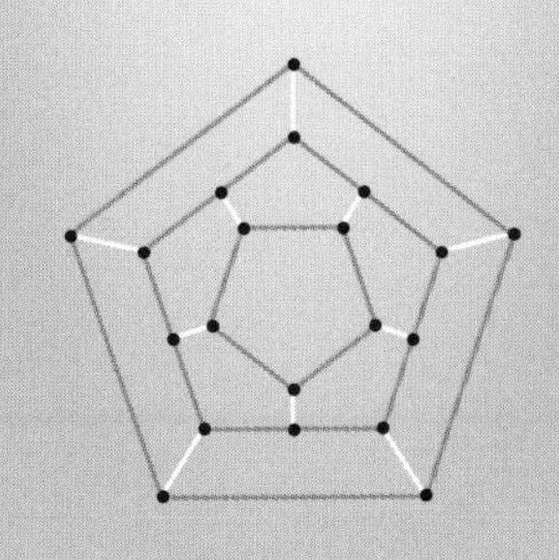

Chapter

4

Tiger, Tiger

From folding paper to make butterfly ink blots, to writing poetry about the "fearful symmetry" of the tiger, we are innately drawn to seeing and creating objects that display symmetry. Mathematically, the study of symmetry now extends well beyond the esthetics of design to being at the heart of notions of our universe.

TESSELLATIONS

The Alhambra palace in Spain is not only beautiful, it is a mathematician's delight. Islamic tradition forbade the representation of living forms, so the artists of the Alhambra used all their ingenuity to create geometric patterns with only compasses and a straight edge. They developed a complex variety of symmetries.

Simple Tilings

In our everyday surroundings, we see surfaces covered with repeated patterns of polygons. Mostly the shapes we see are equilateral triangles or squares or regular hexagons. These shapes all fit together perfectly with no gaps or overlaps. We call this tessellation, where the plane surface can be covered indefinitely in all directions.

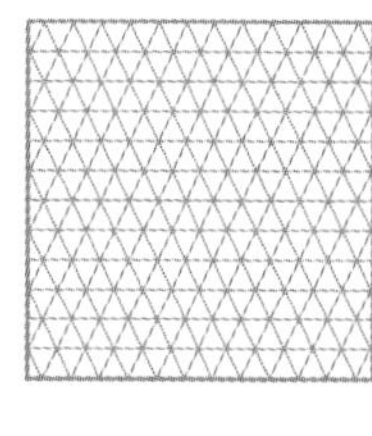

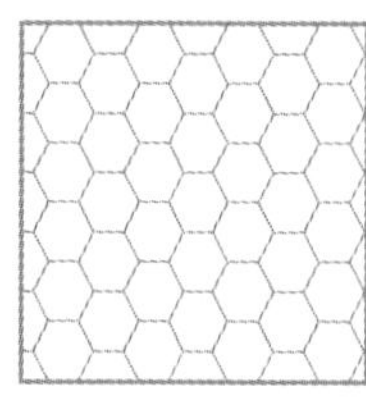

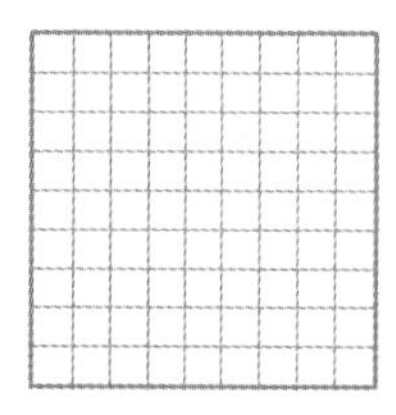

Bees know instinctively that hexagons have the property of tessellating, although bees build honeycombs from hexagons for pragmatic rather than esthetic reasons. The hexagon is the shape with the largest area that tessellates. Circles would actually enclose a greater area but they do not tessellate and do not fit efficiently together. We can show how this works by bundling together seven or more straws. As you apply pressure around the outside of the bundle, the circular cross sections of the straws squash into hexagons.

Pentagonal Tilings

Search around the environment and you will never find a tiling of regular pentagons. Why is that? Examine a pattern of tessellating shapes. You will notice that where the polygons meet, at their vertices, the angles must all add up to 360°. Where four squares meet, there are four angles of 90°. Where six equilateral triangles, meet there are six angles of 60°. For a polygon to tessellate with a similar polygon, the interior angles of the polygon need to be a factor of 360°.

What are the interior angles of a pentagon? We can calculate these by looking at the exterior angles—the angle on the outside of a polygon created by extending one of the edges. Take a pentagon and imagine an ant walking clockwise around its perimeter. At each vertex the ant in continuing its journey will turn through the exterior angle of the pentagon. By the time the ant gets back to where it started from it ends up facing in

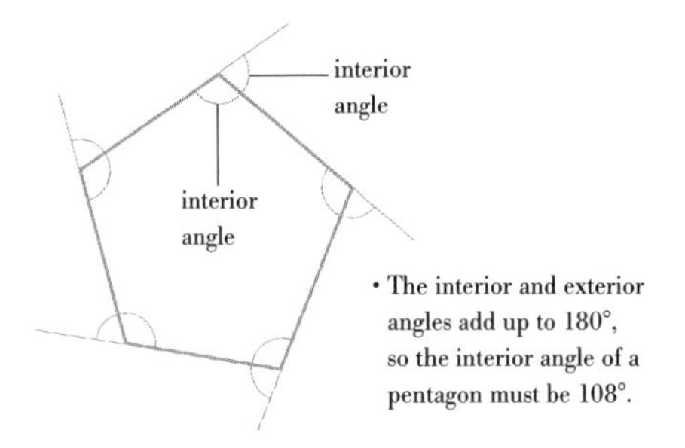

• The interior and exterior angles add up to 180°, so the interior angle of a pentagon must be 108°.

the same direction as it was in the beginning. For this to happen, the ant must have made one complete turn (or a number of complete turns: tracing your finger around the perimeter may convince you that the ant only makes one complete turn). The ant has turned through 360°. Each exterior angle of the regular polygon is the same size, so each exterior angle must be $360° \div 5 = 72°$.

Now that we know the size of the exterior angles, we can work out the size of the interior angles. The exterior and interior angles sit along a straight line, so add up to 180°; hence, the interior angle is 108°. Now we can see why pentagons will not tessellate: 108 will not divide into 360 exactly. Three pentagons fitted together will leave a gap, as they only create 324°, and four would have to overlap.

Incidentally, this result above regarding exterior angles holds for any convex polygon. Regular or not, the exterior angles of a concave polygon always add up to 360°. For a polygon to be convex, a straight line joining any two points on the perimeter will always be entirely within the polygon. For example, all parallelograms are convex, but stars are not (two points on adjacent "arms" of a star cannot be joined by a straight line that is entirely within the star).

The method just used to calculate the interior angle of a regular pentagon can be used for any regular polygon. The six exterior angles of a hexagon total to 360°, so each is 60°, and the interior angle of a regular hexagon is 120°, confirming why the hexagon tessellates.

What about a seven-sided regular polygon (a heptagon)? With seven exterior angles, each will be $360° \div 7 = 51.4°$, giving an interior angle of 128.6°. That certainly won't fit repeatedly to give 360°. We could go on testing polygons of greater number of sides to see if we will find another that will tessellate, but a moment's thought reveals that this search is futile. As the number of sides of the polygon increases, so the size of the exterior angle gets smaller and the interior angle gets bigger. But there is no number greater than 120° that divides exactly in to 360° (apart from 180°, which is a straight line). So there is no regular polygon beyond the hexagon that tessellates.

Although the equilateral triangle, square and regular hexagon are the only three regular polygons that tessellate, as we shall see, things get more interesting when we combine shapes to cover the plane.

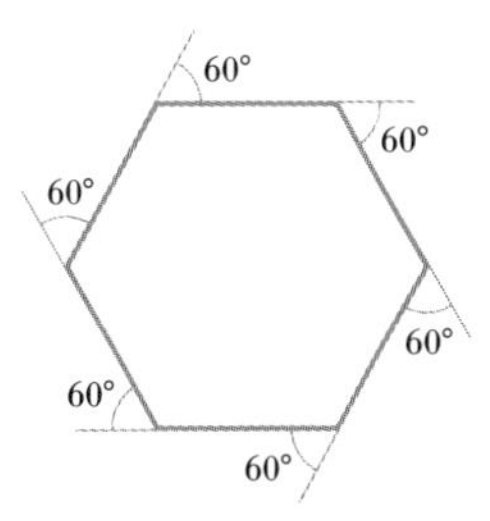

• The regular hexagon is one of the three regular polygons that tessellate.

Floor Tiles

THE PROBLEM:

Domenico manufactures ceramic tiles for floors. He has a range of square and rectangular tiles that he knows tessellate. He wonders if some of the more unusual quadrilaterals, like the trapezoid, will also tessellate.

Are there any quadrilaterals that do not tessellate?

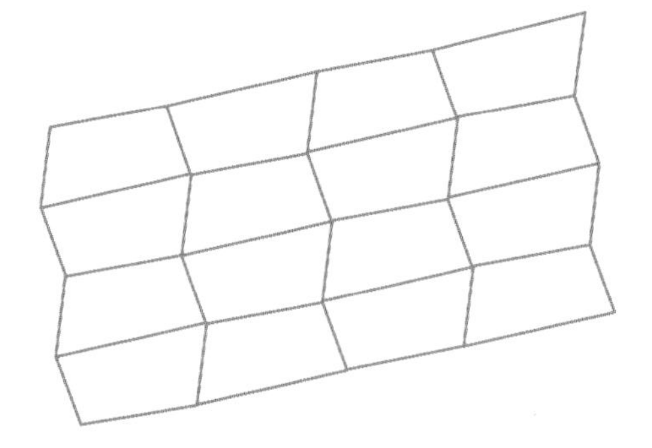

THE METHOD:

If we play around with copies of a trapezoid we soon find that it does tessellate. We can fit the trapezoids together in a long strip by rotating every other one, and then fit together the strips.

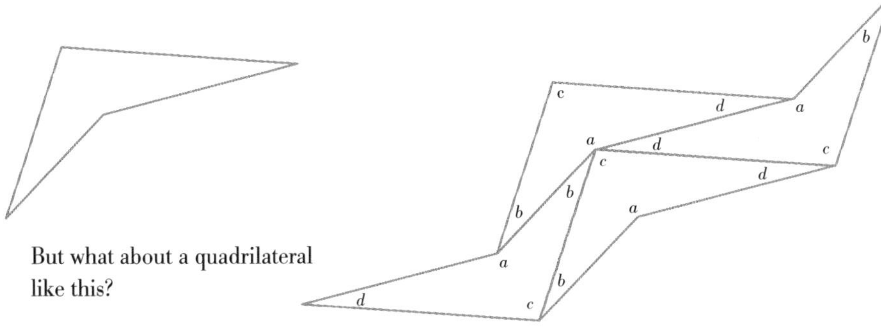

But what about a quadrilateral like this?

It doesn't look as though it will tessellate. We can cut out several and play around with them, and we get a "sort of" tessellation, but we end up with gaps that cannot be filled. We need to be systematic to be convinced that this quadrilateral will not tessellate, so let's look more closely.

The first thing we need to note is that the interior angles of the quadrilateral add up to 360°. We don't need to measure them to know this. We can cut the quadrilateral into two triangles. The sum of the angles in any triangle is 180°. The sum of the angles of two triangles is 360°. If we fit the two triangles together again into the quadrilateral, we can see that the angles of the quadrilateral must also add up to 360°.

For a shape to tessellate, the vertices must fit together to make exactly 360°. Since the four vertices in this quadrilateral add up to 360°, it should tessellate. We need to fit it together with more care. Let's label the angles *a*, *b*, *c*, *d*. By matching up the sides and fitting together all four angles we can get four of these quadrilaterals to fit snugly together around a point.

Now all we have to do is repeat this at every vertex and we do have a tessellation.

THE SOLUTION:

All quadrilaterals tessellate. The jagged edges we get at the edges of the tessellation may mean that not all quadrilaterals make practical tiling for the bathroom floor, however. Squares work best for that!

ARCHIMEDEAN TILINGS

The equilateral triangle, square, and regular hexagon are the only regular polygons that tessellate by themselves. However, anyone familiar with patchwork quilting or Moorish tiling patterns can point to a rich variety of patterns formed by tessellating more than one shape. There is a wealth of geometry behind such patterns.

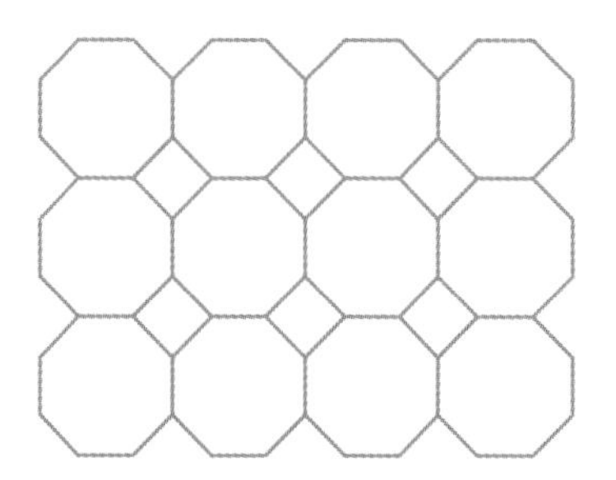

More Complex Tessellations

We know that any quadrilateral will tessellate (pp. 106–107). We have seen that we can put two similar triangles together to create a quadrilateral. It must follow that any triangle will also tessellate.

When we fit regular octagons together, we expect them not to tessellate because their interior angles are too great. But, pleasingly, we can fill the gaps with squares. What regular convex polygons can we combine in a tiling without gaps? Equilateral triangles, squares, and regular hexagons work well together.

Note that at every vertex the same collection of polygons meet and in the same order: hexagon, square, triangle, square. A useful way of recording this arrangement is to note the number of sides in order: (6, 4, 3, 4). Using this notation, the combination of octagons and squares is recorded as (8, 8, 4).

If this seems familiar, it is. We used similar notation with polyhedra (pp. 84–85). There, the five Platonic solids were each made up of only one type of regular polygon. Because of this connection, the three tessellations made from only equilateral triangles, squares, or regular hexagons are known as the

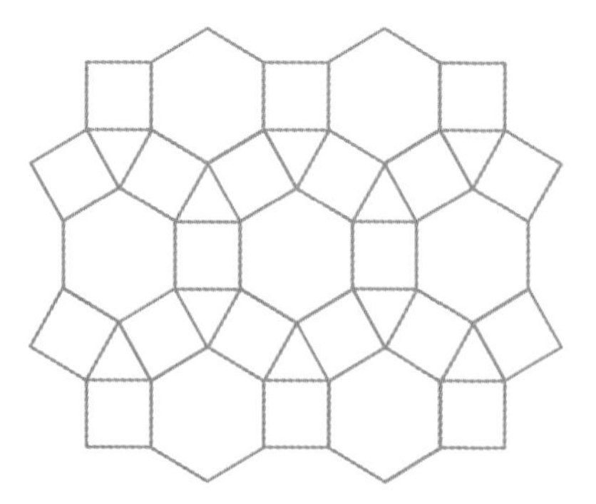

Platonic tessellations. The notation for these is: (3, 3, 3, 3, 3, 3), (4, 4, 4, 4), and (6, 6, 6). You may remember that semiregular polyhedra were made up of more than one polygon, but with vertices all the same, and we used the same notation for these. The same works for semiregular tiling. Together, the regular and semiregular tilings are called Archimedean tilings (again after Archimedes, who first worked on them). Altogether there are 12 Archimedean tilings: the three Platonic tilings and nine other semiregular tilings. Two of the eight semiregular tilings are shown opposite: (4, 8, 8,) and (3, 4, 6, 4). The notation for the other six are below; you might want to sketch them out.

(3, 3, 3, 3, 6), (3, 3, 3, 3, 6), (3, 3, 3, 4, 4), (3, 3, 4, 3, 4), (3, 6, 3, 6), (3, 12, 12), (4, 6, 12).

It is not a mistake that (3, 3, 3, 3, 6) is there twice: there are two different arrangements possible.

• Duals

Just like their three-dimensional counterparts, the Archimedean tilings have dual tilings created by marking the center of each polygon and using these points as vertices of new polygons. We can see that the dual of the tessellation of squares is again a tessellation of squares (self-dual) and that the tessellation of equilateral triangles and tessellation of hexagons are duals of each other. A particularly pleasing dual arises from the (3, 3, 4, 3, 4) tiling of triangles and squares (known as the "snub square tiling"). Its dual turns out to be a tessellation of non-regular pentagons—the Cairo pentagonal tiling.

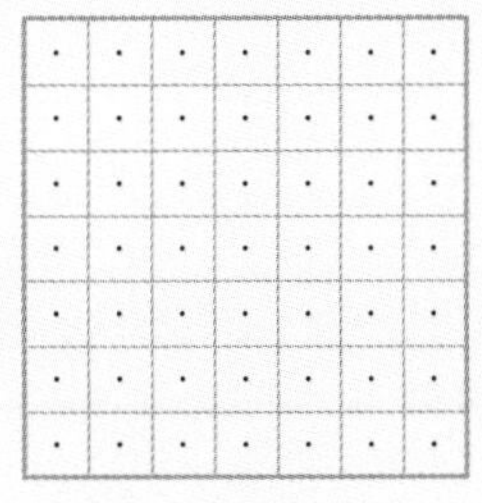

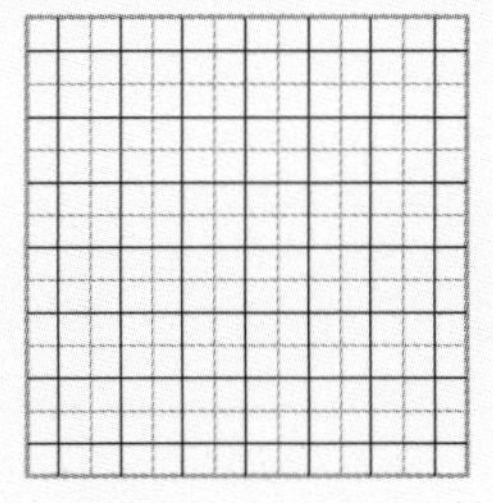

• If we mark the center of each green square and join these we get a tessellation of black squares, and vice versa. The two square tilings are duals of each other.

• In the tiling of square and triangles, five polygons meet at every vertex (4, 3, 3, 4, 3). Marking the center of each of these and joining these points produces the dual tiling of Cairo pentagons.

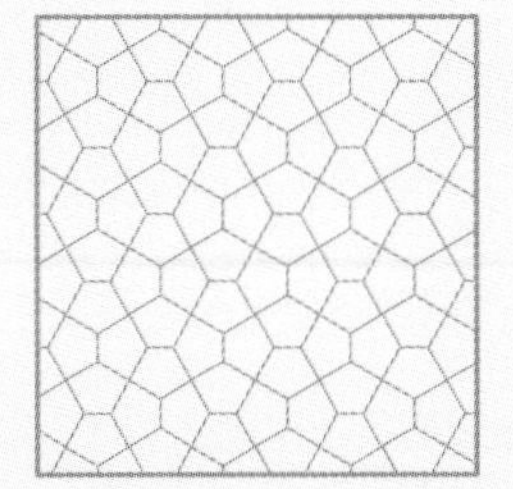

Periodic Prints

THE PROBLEM:

Susie is a printmaker and would like to print out a length of fabric with a design based around this tessellation.

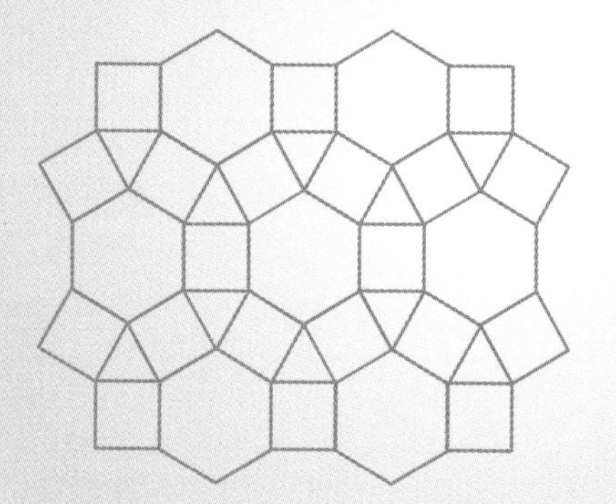

She wants to create as few printing blocks as possible. What is the smallest number she needs?

THE METHOD:

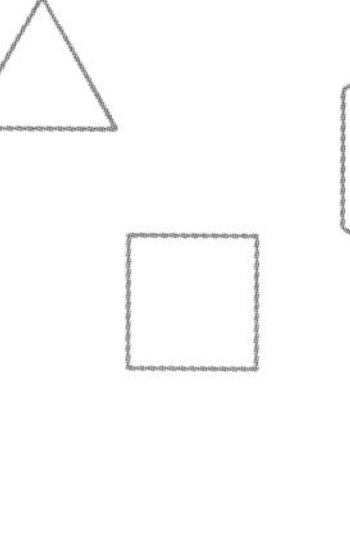

Clearly Susie could make three blocks: a triangle, a square, and a hexagon and repeatedly use these. That would work but be rather fiddly and time-consuming.

Looking at the tessellation, one unified element does seem to stand out.

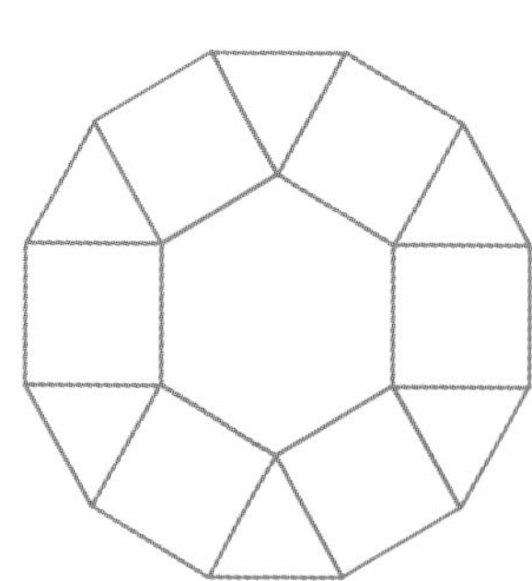

A block could be made of this, but when printing the motif will overlap with those already printed so very careful alignment would be required.

Taking a portion of the large motif does provide Susie with a single tile that can be used to generate the entire design.

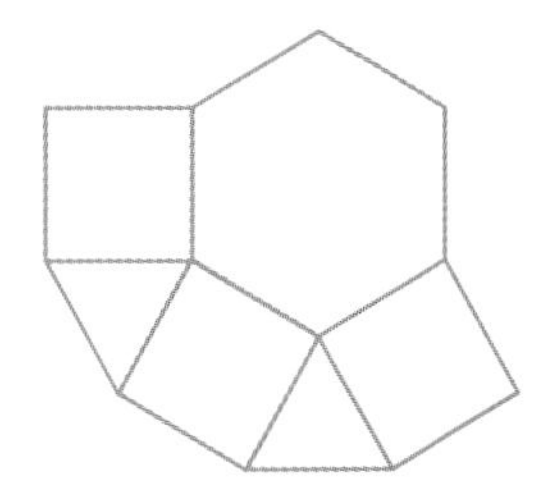

This tile provides the "fundamental region" for generating the entire design.

For a tile like this to be a fundamental region it has to have the following properties:

- It is the smallest size possible.
- It does not have to overlap with other regions.
- The tiling can be created simply by copying the tile by sliding (translating it) to a new position without needing to rotate or reflect it.
- A tiling that can be created in this way from a fundamental region is known as a periodic tiling.

THE SOLUTION:

The tiling that Susie wants to recreate is a periodic tiling and it can be reproduced using only one fundamental region. Such templates are known as "girih" templates. Mathematicians now think that they were used to create Islamic tiling patterns, rather than each design being constructed from scratch using only a straight edge and compasses.

WALLPAPER PATTERNS

We have looked at some of the mathematics behind tiling our floors. How about decorating our walls? There may be a limited number of ways to tessellate tiles, but surely there are an infinite number of possibilities for wallpaper designs? Setting aside the fact that there are clearly an unlimited number of motifs and colors for wallpaper, the underlying mathematics shows that there are in essence only 17 different basic patterns.

Stenciling

Before exploring the mathematics of wallpaper, let us look at the designs that we might create with a stencil. Take this as our basic shape.

The first design we might make is simply created by repeating the motif by moving it regularly up, down, or along—by translating it. We can also turn the stencil to rotate the motif as we translate it. We can flip our stencil over as we translate is, so we can also reflect the motif.

School mathematics often suggests that these are the three basic options that we have: translate, rotate, and reflect. But there is one further option: a glide reflection.

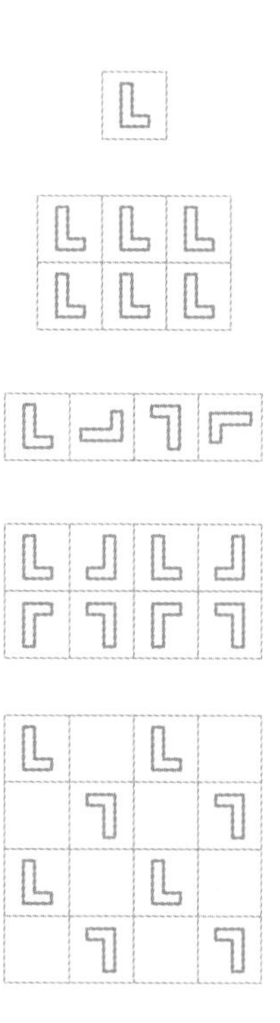

This glide reflection is made by translating the motif and then reflecting it—but then, so was the reflection design above, so what is the difference? The glide reflection is essentially different because we have ended up with an overall design that has no axis of symmetry. There is nowhere on this design where we could place a mirror and the result of looking in the mirror would look the same as it would without the mirror. We can do this with the earlier reflection.

These four basic design moves—translation, rotation, reflection, and glide reflection—are called the isometries or rigid motions. They are the only operations that we can apply to a plane shape and leave the measurements of the shape unchanged (all lengths and angles are preserved). We call all of these symmetries because the size of the original motif is preserved.

Translations and rotations are known as direct symmetries, and reflections and glide reflections as indirect symmetries as these latter two reverse a figure: our L motif is no longer in the orientation of an L after reflecting it.

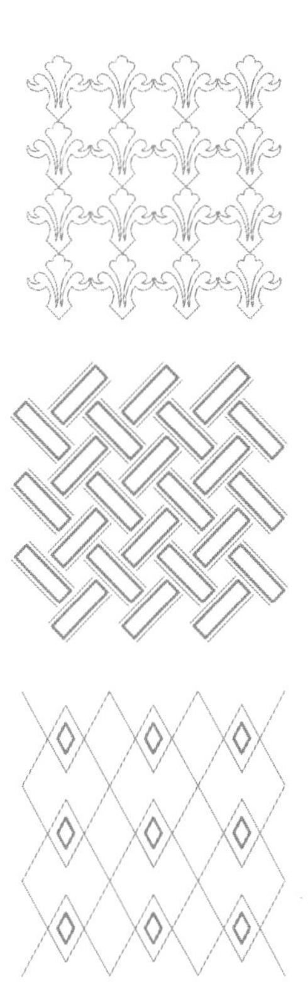

Wallpaper Designs

These four symmetries (translation, rotation, reflection, and glide reflection) are now all we need to create wallpapers. Setting aside rotations for the moment, we can make wallpaper by translation alone; translation followed by reflection, and reflection followed by glide reflection.

If we introduce rotations, there are only four "orders" of rotation that are possible that make everything fit neatly. Order of rotation is the number of ways that a motif can be turned and look the same. The first design below has order of rotation 3: the second order of rotation 4.

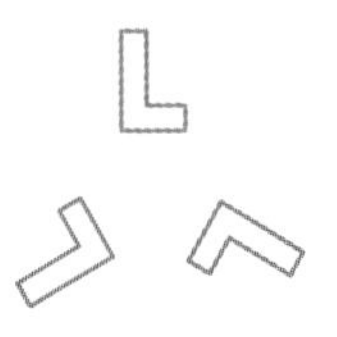

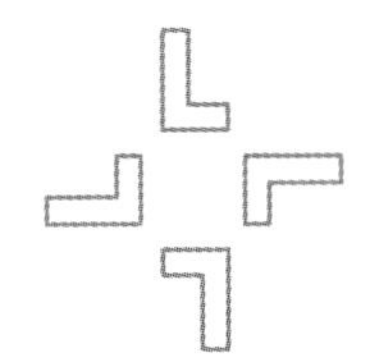

We can create wallpapers with order of rotation 2, 3, 4, and 6. (Strictly speaking, 1 should be included here as every design has order of rotation 1, but that does not lead to interesting designs). Why stop at six? We saw earlier that no regular polygon with more than six sides can tessellate the plane. For similar reasons (too complicated to enter into here), it is not possible for a design to have orders of rotation *r* greater than six. Combining these rotational symmetries with translations, reflections, and glide reflections results in only 14 other possible wallpapers.

Profile

M. C. Escher

Escher was a Dutch graphic artist who developed, through his art, an interest in the geometry of symmetry. He was not mathematically educated, yet he learned and developed a deep understanding of symmetry, and later of topology. As his ideas progressed, he furthered his ideas by discussing them with contemporary mathematicians: Pólya, Coxeter, and Penrose.

The Life of Escher

Maurits Cornelis Escher, nicknamed Mauk, was born in 1898 in Leeuwarden, the Netherlands. As a child his health was poor and his education suffered—in particular, he showed no capability for mathematics. He found numbers and letters confusing, but he developed a feeling for two- and three-dimensional shapes. His family hoped he would become an architect, but instead he studied decorative arts, drawing and woodcut techniques.

When he was 24, he traveled through Italy and Spain, a journey that greatly influenced his later work. He married and lived in Rome until 1935, when the political situation under Mussolini forced him to move first to Switzerland and then to Belgium. During the war he moved to the Netherlands.

By 1958 Escher had achieved great fame. He lectured, corresponded, and exhibited, as well as developing and producing his own work. He died in 1972.

Escher and Mathematics

During 1936, Escher and his wife took a sea trip to Spain where he made his second visit to the palace of Alhambra in Granada, Spain, and visited the mosque in Cordoba. This formed a significant point in Escher's work, when he moved from landscapes to "mental imagery"—the graphical works and the tilings. He said later that his trip to the Alhambra "was the richest source of inspiration I have ever tapped."

Using the sketches that he and his wife made at the Alhambra, he created geometric grids using his own characters such as birds, lions, and fish. When his brother Berend saw his woodcuts, he encouraged Escher to study symmetry and sent him Pólya's academic paper on symmetry groups. Escher grasped the wallpaper group of 17 plane symmetries visually and intuitively. He had found examples of all 17 symmetries in the decorations of the Alhambra, created by the Islamic Moors in the

• A tiling of birds. Escher drew inspiration from the natural and often featured animals, such as birds and fish, in his artwork.

13th century. Escher worked on a range of symmetry types and kept detailed, idiosyncratic records of shape, color, and symmetrical properties. Without realizing it, he was exploring ideas of what mathematicians later called "crystallography" (crystallography is the branch of science that studies the formation and structure of crystals). In 1941 he published a paper, "Regular Division of the Plane with Asymmetric Congruent Polygons," in which he worked through his mathematical ideas. In spite of Escher's poor mathematical education, he is considered a research mathematician from the ideas set out in this paper, and because of his subsequent work.

He wrote, "At first I had no idea at all of the possibility of systematically building up my figures. I did not know ... this was possible for someone untrained in mathematics, and especially as a result of my putting forward my own layman's theory, which forced me to think through the possibilities."

Later, he worked with the mathematician Roger Penrose to develop his ideas on topology, which led to works such as *Castrovalva*, *Waterfall*, and *Up and Down*. Their collaboration led Penrose to devise an impossible triangle, the Penrose triangle, which Escher subsequently used in many of his works (see Penrose Triangle, p. 119).

Hyperbolic Geometry

From 1956, Escher worked on how to represent infinity on a two-dimensional plane. He discussed the problem with mathematician Donald Coxeter, who introduced the idea of hyperbolic tessellations (regular tilings in the hyperbolic plane). To compare hyperbolic geometry with Euclidean geometry, think of two straight lines in a two-dimensional plane that are both perpendicular to a third line: In Euclidean geometry, the lines remain at a constant distance from each other, and are known as parallels.

In hyperbolic geometry, they curve away from each other; these lines are often called ultraparallels.

In elliptic geometry, the lines curve toward each other and eventually intersect.

You can picture hyperbolic geometry by imagining the shapes drawn on curved surfaces, such as on the surface of a sphere or the inside surface of a bowl.

Escher's works *Circle Limit I–IV* show his work on hyperbolic tessellations. Coxeter wrote about Escher's drawings, "Escher got it absolutely right to the millimeter ... He has achieved mathematical perfection."

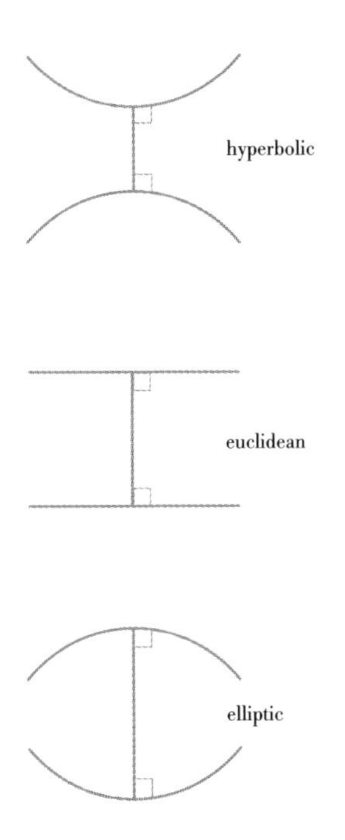

Exercise 20 Escher Tiling

THE PROBLEM:

Jamie designs cutters for making unusual shaped cookies. His collection includes stars and crescent moons. Seeing some of Escher's designs, Jamie would like to design a cutter that will produce biscuits that could be tiled like an Escher design and iced to look like creatures, say birds or fish. How can he set about designing such a tile?

THE METHOD:

Escher-style tessellations can be created by simple transformations of the basic tiling of equilateral triangles or squares. Here is how to create a tile that will tessellate with the outline of a fish.

Starting from a piece of square card, a line is drawn between adjacent corners that resembles, vaguely, the head of a fish.

This is cut out and slid (translated) to the opposite side of the square and taped into position there. On the bottom edge of the square, a line resembling a fin is drawn. In a similar fashion, this piece is cut off and translated to the opposite edge.

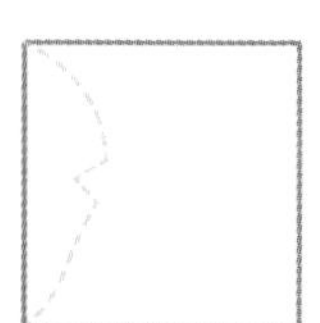

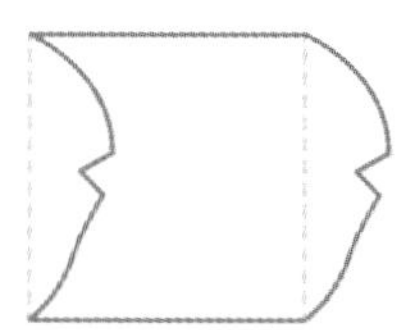

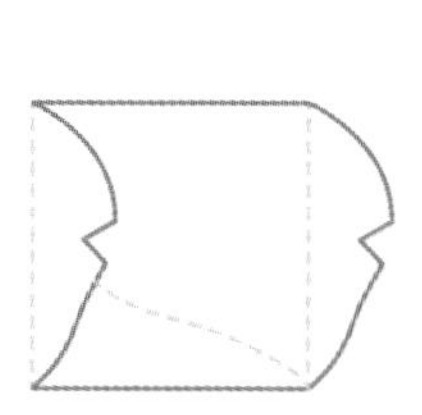

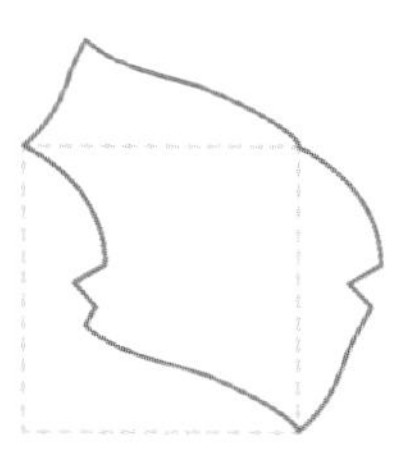

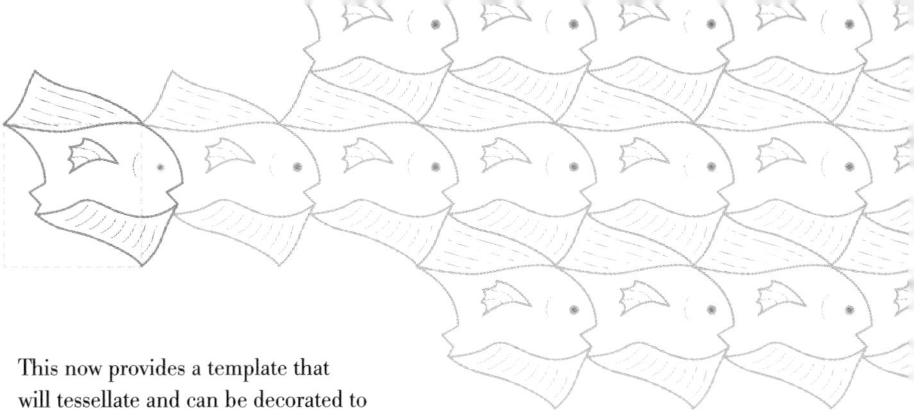

This now provides a template that will tessellate and can be decorated to create a shoal of fishes.

The construction of these fish templates results in a repeating (periodic) pattern where all the fishes are facing in the same direction. A different result occurs if the pieces cut out are rotated into a new position.

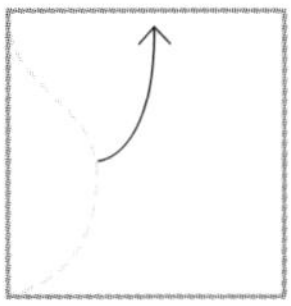

Starting again from a unit card square, a piece is cut out but this time rotated to fit on an adjacent edge.

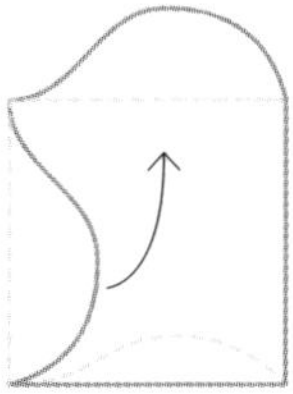

Repeating this with another edge gives the outline of a stingray.

Decorated and tessellated, a collection of these tiles produces a shoal of stingrays that are swimming against each other.

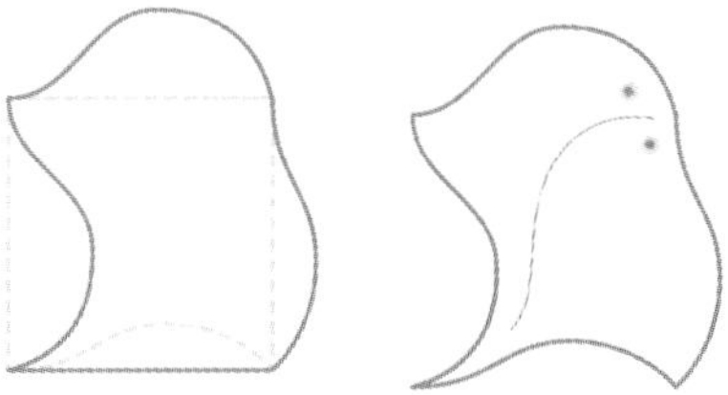

THE SOLUTION:

Jamie can produce templates for tessellating cookies by simple adaptations of the square. He can produce other variations by applying similar techniques to an equilateral triangle.

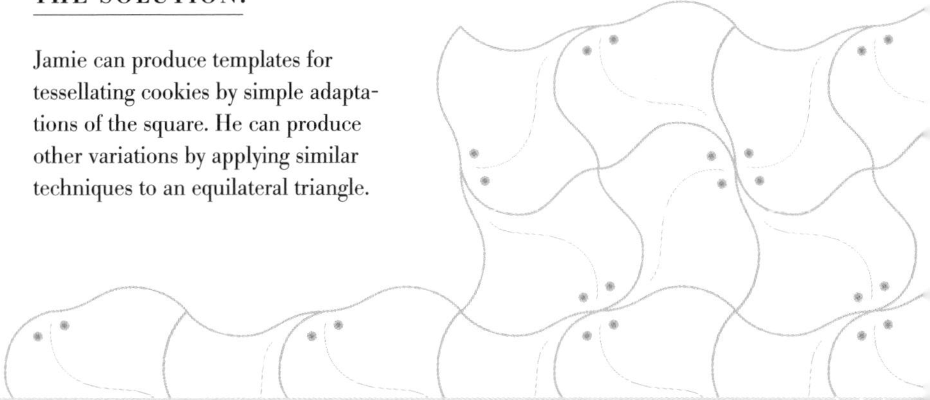

Profile

Roger Penrose

Roger Penrose is an English mathematical physicist and cosmologist, and Emeritus Rouse Ball Professor of Mathematics at Oxford University. Most of his work has been in the area of quantum physics and relativity theory, including work on black holes, but he has also pursued an interest in recreational mathematics, specifically in algebraic geometry. He has made major contributions to mathematics and physics.

The Life of Penrose

Roger Penrose was born in 1931 in Essex. His father was a geneticist and his mother a doctor. He studied mathematics at University College London, and gained a PhD from Cambridge University in algebraic geometry. He became interested in physics, and in 1959 he published a series of important papers on cosmology.

In 1966, Penrose was appointed Professor of Applied Mathematics at Birkbeck College, London. Penrose worked on quantum theory and relativity, and he combined them with what is called twistor theory. Twistor

- **PUBLICATIONS**

Penrose's popular science books are concerned with the non-algorithmic processes of human thought and the quantum effects in the brain that are the source of our consciousness.

The Emperor's New Mind: Concerning Computers, Minds, and the Laws of Physics *(1989): Penrose summarizes modern physics, attacks the notion of artificial intelligence, and argues that the human mind cannot be simulated by computers or anything algorithmic.*

Shadows of the Mind: A Search for the Missing Science of Consciousness *(1994): continues the exploration of what modern physics tells us about the mind, and builds on the arguments against artificial intelligence.*

The Nature of Space and Time *(with Stephen Hawking, 1996): a collection of lectures given by Penrose and Hawking in 1994 that explores the functions of mathematics and physics within the field of cosmology.*

The Road to Reality: A Complete Guide to the Laws of the Universe *(2007): explores the connections between mathematics and the physical world through hyperbolic geometry, complex numbers, complex calculus, and so on. It is arguably Penrose's most ambitious and farthest reaching work*

The novelist Brian Aldiss collaborated with Penrose in his science fiction novel White Mars, *where Penrose provided the content on particle physics.*

• The Penrose triangle. Roger Penrose described it as "impossibility in its purest form."

theory combines algebraic and geometric methods, and is a major contribution to this area of physics. Penrose has also introduced a coordinate system to theoretical physics, called Penrose diagrams. These are two-dimensional diagrams that represent the relationship between different points in space-time. The diagrams use a coordinate system where the vertical axis represents time and the horizontal axis represents space, and they are used to illustrate the space-time environment of black holes. He has collaborated with Stephen Hawking on the study of black holes.

Penrose has been awarded numerous prizes and honors for his work, and in 1994 he was knighted for his contributions to science.

Recreational Mathematics

In 1954 Penrose, with his father Lionel Penrose, published a paper on "Impossible figures." He sent this paper to Escher, who incorporated Penrose's two impossible figures—the Penrose triangle and the Penrose staircase in subsequent designs.

DAINA TAIMINA

Daina Taimina is a Latvian mathematician at Cornell University who crochets objects to represent hyperbolic space. She specializes in creating large, mathematically precise, symmetrical hyperbolic planes. Hyperbolic planes curve away from each other, unlike curves on a sphere, which curve toward each other. Daina Taimina explored how these planes work by increasing at an exponential rate the number of stitches in the crochet. The crocheted results look like coral reefs—there is a connection between the crochet and the natural world. Hyperbolic geometry maximizes surface area and minimizes volume. Corals, for example, need a large surface area to feed from.

• Hyperspace meets needlepoint, with surprisingly captivating results.

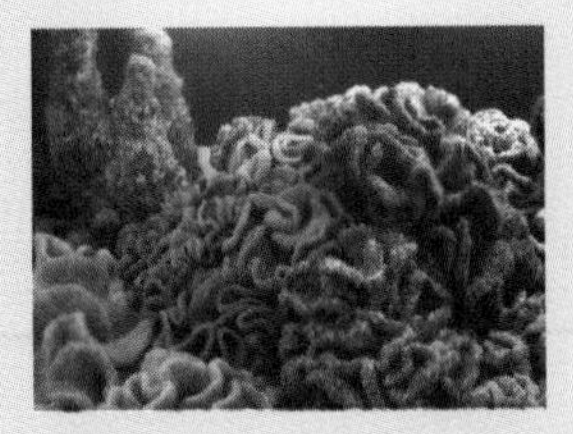

PENROSE TILES

We saw earlier (pp. 104–105) that only three regular polygons tile without gaps or overlap: the equilateral triangle, the square and the regular hexagon. The "missing" regular pentagon, which cannot tile, led to mathematicians assuming that nature would follow this and that crystals would form with rotational symmetries of only two-, three-, four-, and six-fold. But nature is not constrained by mathematicians.

Kites and Darts

Roger Penrose approached looking at tilings from a different perspective. The tilings that give rise to wallpaper patterns (see pp. 112–113) all cover the plane in a regular, repeating fashion. He played around with the problem of tessellating with a set of tiles that would cover a surface without gaps or overlaps and without generating a repeating pattern: the study of quasi-symmetry. In 1619 Johannes Kepler had shown that the gaps left when tiling with a regular pentagon could be filled with five-pointed star polygons (pentagrams), decagons and other polygons; inspired by this, Penrose puzzled over this problem for many years. Penrose's first tiling used pentagons and three other shapes: a pentagram, a "boat" (roughly 3/5 of a star) and a "thin" rhombus or "diamond." Eventually, in 1974, Penrose found two shapes, now called the Penrose tiles, which tessellate in a five-fold non-repeating symmetry. Both tiles were derived from the regular

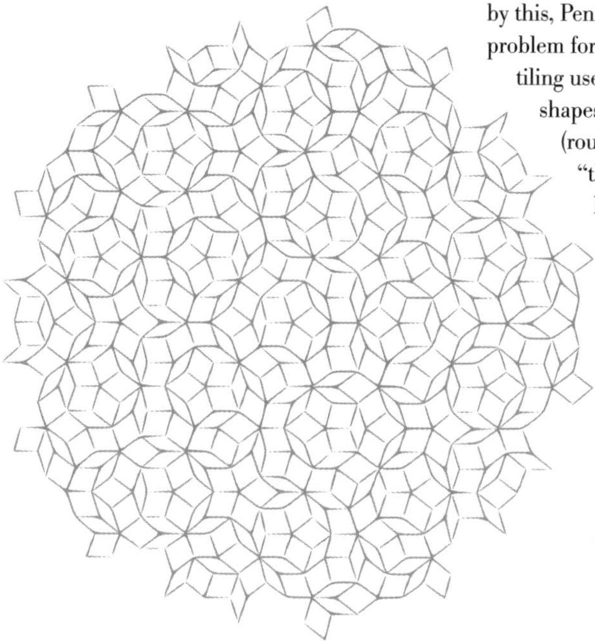

• Two different types of rhombi make up this non-periodic Penrose tiling.

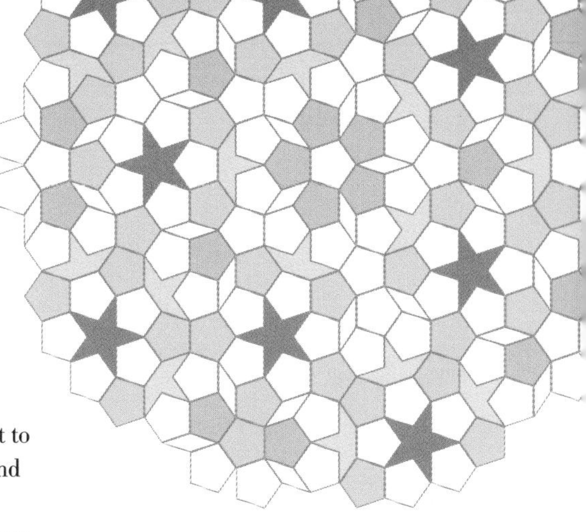

pentagon and became known as the Penrose kite and dart tiles.

The tilings arising from combinations of these tiles are created by following "matching rules" that prevent simple repetitive patterns emerging. From these rules a huge range of highly complicated patterns emerge. Two, and only two, of these tilings turn out to have five-fold rotational symmetry, and are called the star and sun patterns. Rotating each of the star and sun tilings through 72° it looks identical, but that tiling lacks what is known as translational symmetry: a copy shifted away from the center of rotation can never be positioned so that it matches the original exactly. As Martin Gardner, the author and popularizer of mathematics, noted, as you move out from the center of rotation, it looks as though the tilings are "striving to repeat themselves but never quite making it."

It turns out that such patterns do exist in nature and "quasicrystals" can form with fivefold symmetry. Unlike most crystals, these are not formed from a regular lattice but they do naturally come into being. And quasicrystals have some interesting properties: metal ones are poor heat conductors and are useful in creating nonstick surfaces.

Like a lot of mathematics, it appears that such tilings are not entirely new. There is evidence of tilings similar to Penrose tilings in Islamic art some 500 years old.

EARLY GIRIH TILINGS

Harvard physics graduate student Peter Lu studied the intricate geometric "girih" patterns on the 800-year-old buildings in Uzbekistan. Writing in *Science*, he suggests that the tiling patterns involve mathematical ideas that were only formally set out hundreds of years later. Lu argues that the tiling patterns were made differently than had previously been thought. If the tilers had been drawing directly on the walls, as was judged to be the case, then given the large walls of patterns produced you would expect evidence of errors committed. Lu, however, observed that the patterns are amazingly perfect, even over very large surfaces. Reminded of his study of Penrose tiles, Lu went on to find evidence of informal knowledge of such tilings.

Exercise 21 Reptiles

THE PROBLEM:

Playing around with a collection of plastic tiles, Valerie notices that putting four squares together creates a larger version of the tile. She knew that putting, say, four hexagons together would not form a larger hexagon. Did this only work for squares?

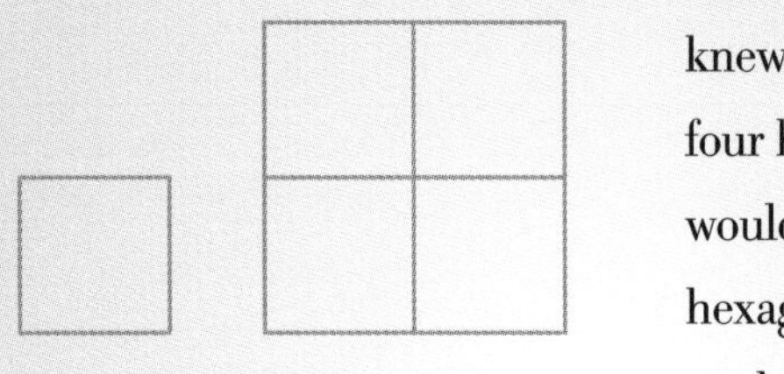

For which of these other tiles can four copies of the tile be put together to create a larger version of the original tile? You can turn tiles over if need be.

THE METHOD:

Like the square, four copies of the equilateral triangle are easily put together to create a larger version of itself.

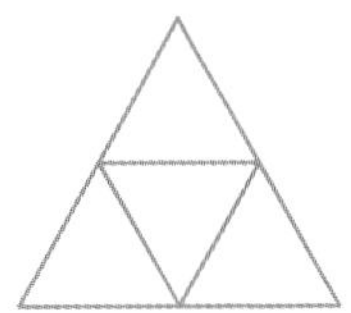

Since the pentagon does not tessellate the plane, fitting four of these together without any gaps cannot be done, so a larger version of itself is not possible. The hexagon does tessellate and four copies of the hexagon do fit together, but they do not create a larger hexagon.

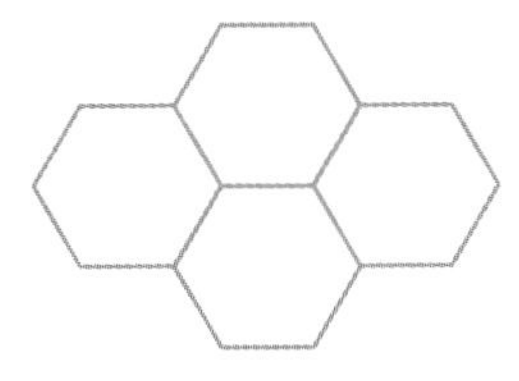

Playing around with the symmetrical trapezoid (or trapezium as some call it), a larger version of itself quickly emerges. And the other trapezoids are also self-replicating.

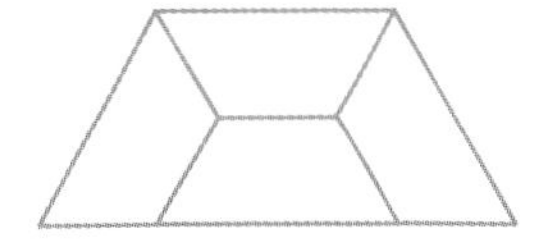

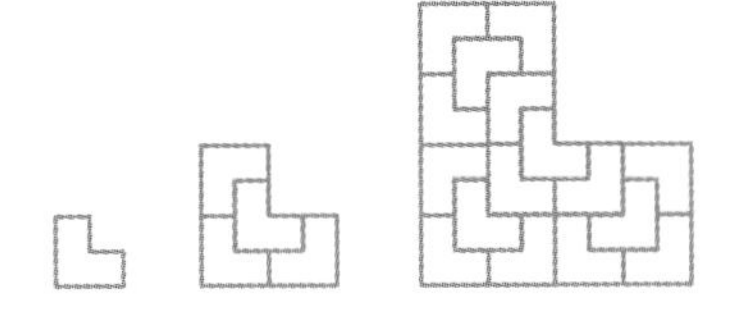

The L-shapes can also be used to create larger versions of themselves.

The last tile is known as the "Sphinx" from its outline resembling the famous Egyptian monument. It's not immediately obvious, but this too is self-replicating.

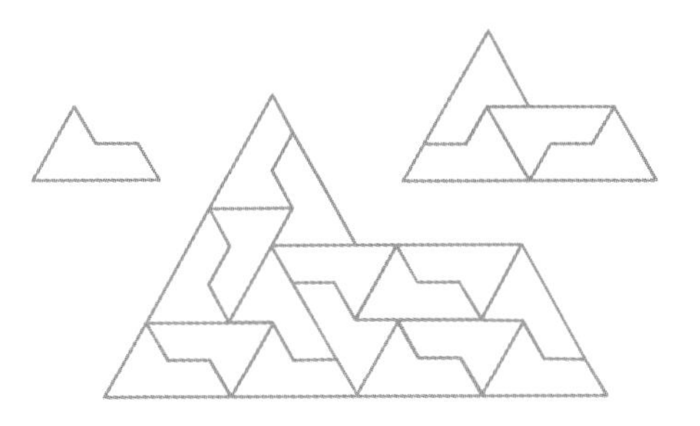

THE SOLUTION:

Tiles that have the property that combining several copies creates a larger version of themselves are called rep-tiles, abbreviated from "replicating tiles." Solomon Golomb invented the L-shaped rep-tile, which fits together to form an L-shape.

So it turns out that the Sphinx is not half-woman, half-beast but a reptile!

Profile Martin Gardner

Martin Gardner developed a lifelong interest in recreational mathematics, and immersed himself in it for most of his life. He wrote the mathematical games column in *Scientific American* from 1956 to 1981, and he wrote over 70 books about recreational mathematics. He said of himself, "I just play all the time and am just fortunate enough to get paid for it."

The Life of Martin Gardner

Gardner was born in 1914 and was brought up in Oklahoma. He went to the University of Chicago, where he studied philosophy. He graduated in 1936, at the height of the Depression, and took odd jobs until the Second World War, when he joined the U.S. Navy. After the war he earned a living writing magazine and newspaper articles, including writing articles for a children's periodical, *Humpty Dumpty's Magazine*. In the 1950s he moved to a good mathematical address, Euclid Avenue, in New York, with his wife and two sons. In 1979 he and his wife moved to North Carolina in semiretirement, and, when his wife died, he moved to live near his son in Oklahoma. He received a number of honors in his lifetime for his work. He died in 2010.

Gardner's Works

In 1956 Gardner wrote *Mathematics, Magic and Mystery*, one of the first of his 70 books on recreational mathematics, and a successful article for *Scientific American* on hexaflexagons. This led to his monthly column on mathematical games, which he wrote for 25 years. A whole generation of mathematicians grew up reading Gardner's column, and there were many who bought *Scientific American* just for the Mathematical Games. Gardner's writing popularized mathematics in North America, and the titles of some of his books give a flavor of his writing: *The Annotated Alice* (1970), *Mathematical Circus* (1979), *Knotted Doughnuts and Other Mathematical Entertainments* (1986), *Hexaflexagons and Other Mathematical Diversions* (1988), *Perplexing Puzzles and Tantalising Teasers* (1989), *From Penrose Tiles to the Trapdoor* (1989), *Mathematical Puzzles and Diversions* (1991), *Origami*, and *Eleusis and the Soma Cube* (2008).

He also wrote several books debunking what Gardner termed pseudoscience, such as *Fads and Fallacies in the Name of Science* (1957), and *Did Adam and Eve have Navels?* (2001).

"I had no formal training in mathematics, only an amateur's passion for its marvels, and admiration and awe for its leaders... I enjoy mathematics so much because it has a strange kind of unearthly beauty."—***Martin Gardner***

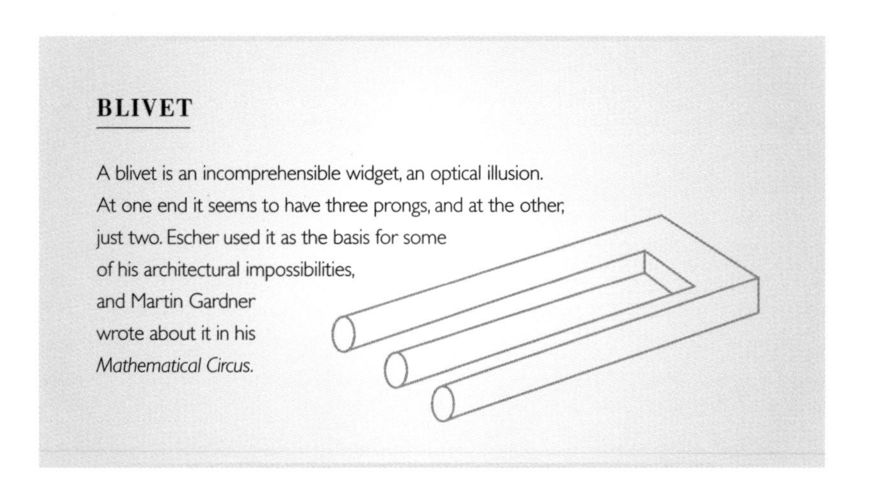

BLIVET

A blivet is an incomprehensible widget, an optical illusion. At one end it seems to have three prongs, and at the other, just two. Escher used it as the basis for some of his architectural impossibilities, and Martin Gardner wrote about it in his *Mathematical Circus.*

A Lifetime in Recreational Mathematics

Gardner had no mathematical qualifications beyond high school, but was always fascinated by mathematical puzzles and problems. When he was a child, his father gave him a copy of Sam Lloyd's *Cyclopedia of Puzzles*, and one of his first interests was magic and magic tricks—and these interests stayed with him all his life.

Gardner met a range of interesting mathematicians while he worked for *Scientific American*, influencing public interest in their work, and he also popularized various mathematical subjects. He helped to publicize the work of Escher (see pp. 114–115); he made the public aware of the Penrose tiles (see pp. 120–121) and Conway's The Game of Life; he introduced flexagons, the Soma cube, Polyominoes, tangrams, fractals, the board game "Hex," and code-breaking.

Rep-tiles

Tiling is a major theme in recreational mathematics—we have seen how Penrose played around with tiles to find the Penrose tiles. Solomon Golomb was another mathematician who was fascinated by tiling, and Martin Gardner also wrote about his work. Golomb invented polyominoes, inspiration for the game Tetris, and rep-tiles. Recreational mathematicians have played around to find more and more interesting rep-tiles.

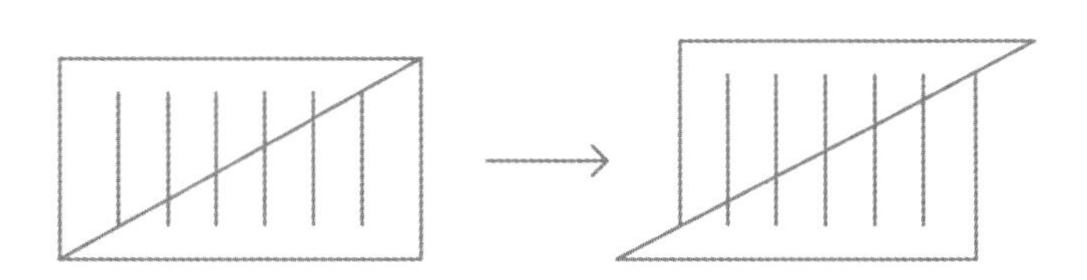

Chapter

Sunday in the Park

Although the origins of Euclidean geometry were established using only the basic tools of a pair of compasses and a straight edge, Euclidean geometry is essentially concerned with measurement: angle sizes and lengths of sides. Euclidean geometry at heart is quantitative. Interest in Sunday afternoon strolls and the relationships between people at a party provided the origins of a new type of qualitative geometry: the study of networks.

Visiting the Museum

THE PROBLEM:

Vincent is visiting an art exhibition. Here is a map of the rooms. He wonders if he can wander round and pass through each door once and once only. (He is happy to visit the same room more than once.) What route can Vincent take?

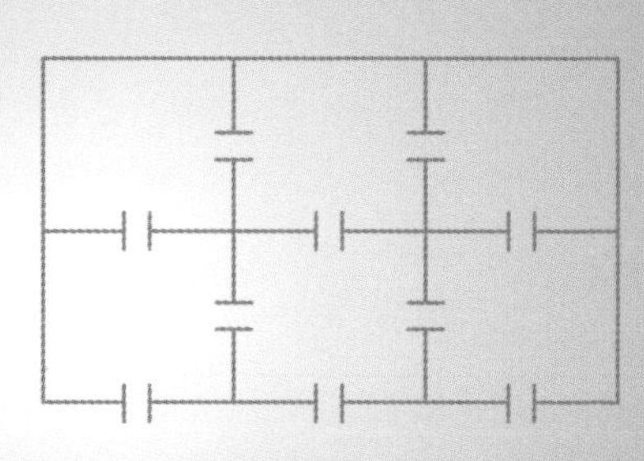

THE METHOD:

Sketching out the plan and tracing through a route makes it clear that Vincent's challenge is non-trivial. Wherever you start, you end up getting stuck in one of the rooms.

In fact, it is impossible to find a route through this exhibition going through each door once and once only. To see why, label each room, A to F. We need to include the outside space as well, so label that G.

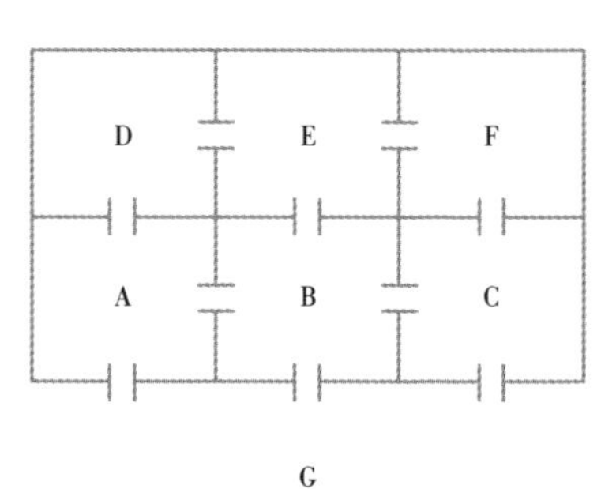

We are more interested in the doors—the connections between rooms—than the rooms themselves. So we can produce a rather different "map" of the exhibition, reducing the rooms to points ("nodes") and representing doors by lines—edges—joining the nodes.

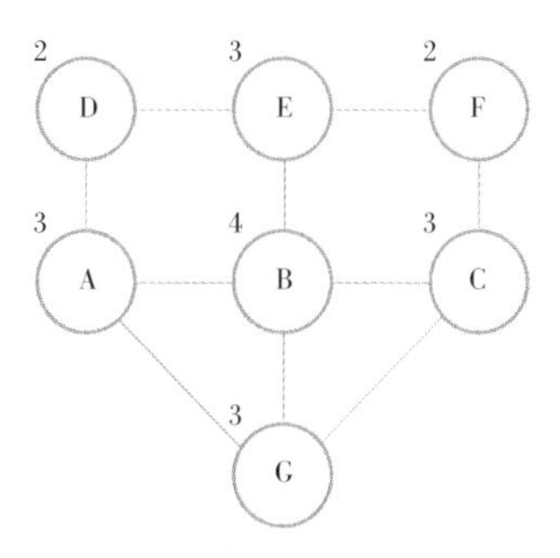

In this network, room A has three doors, shown by the three edges joining A to B, D and G. The number of edges coming from a node is called the valency of that node. Node A has valency 3, node B has valency 4 and so on.

Returning to the exhibition, we make the obvious but important observation that when Vincent enters, say, room D, he also has to leave it. The node for that room has valency 2, that is, an even-numbered valency. Vincent can enter and exit Room B twice, so that room has valency 4.

Room E, on the other hand, is different. It has a node of valency 3. That means that Vincent can enter and leave once, but has to enter once more—but cannot exit except by a door he has already used. Hence, any room with an odd-numbered valency means that one door will have to be used twice.

Which rooms have odd valencies? Four: A (3), C (3), E (3), G (3). Even if he starts in one of these rooms, Vincent will get stuck in one of the other "odd" rooms before he can visit them all.

THE SOLUTION:

Vincent cannot visit all the rooms and go through each door once and once only. He will just have to enjoy the pictures instead.

THE BRIDGES OF KÖNIGSBERG

The museum problem is an example of the mathematical study of networks, also known as graph theory. The map of the exhibition (p. 129) does not look much like the graphs we see in newspapers of election polls, but that's mathematics for you. Graph theory began in earnest when Leonhard Euler (see pp. 132–133) took an interest in the popular afternoon stroll around the town of Königsberg.

Then in Prussia, Königsberg spanned both banks of the river Pregel, which had two islands in it. Seven bridges linked the islands and riverbanks.

The story is that the good citizens of Königsberg liked a Sunday stroll that took them across the bridges but that no one had been able to find a route that would allow them to cross each bridge once and once only. Euler become intrigued by this challenge and finally put the matter to rest in 1735 when he showed why no such route could exist. Somewhat surprisingly, this was like no other problem that mathematicians had ever tackled before and Euler brought new insights to bear. First of all, he reduced the situation to its bare essentials. Euler saw that the actual dimensions and layout of the river, banks, and islands were all irrelevant. All that really mattered were the places that a walker could be and the connections between these. In essence, there are only four places a walker can be—on either of the banks or on either of the islands. These can be reduced to nodes (or vertices) and the bridges shown by lines (edges) joining them. The map of the town and bridges is reduced, stripping out everything except the features relevant to the problem.

From this network representation Euler was able to show why the only-once-over-each-bridge challenge was impossible. He started off by observing that there could be two types of tours across the bridges. You could

• The seven bridges of Königsberg, joining the islands of Kneiphof and Lomse to each other, and to the north and south banks.

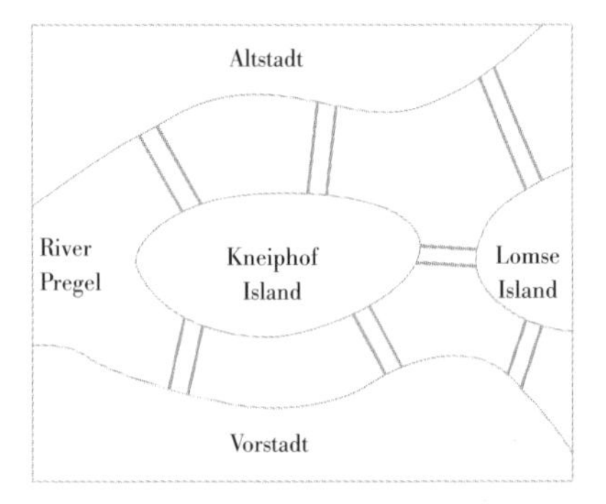

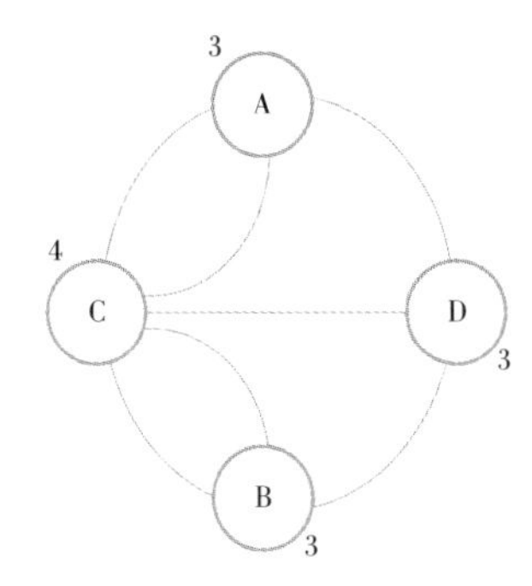

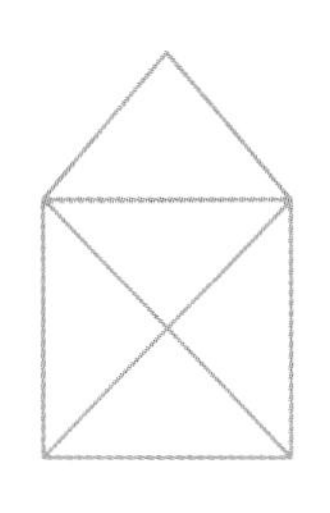

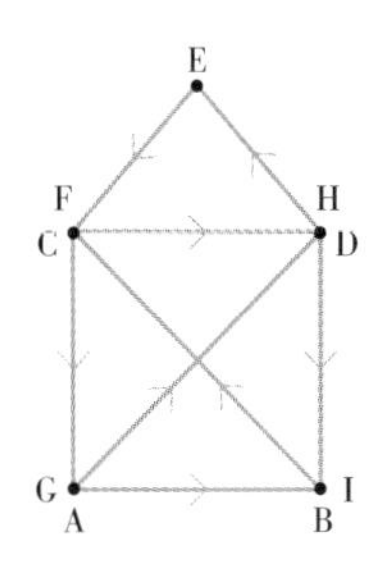

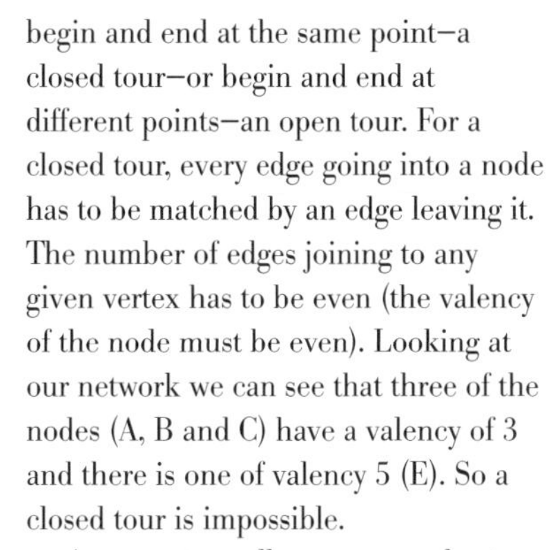

begin and end at the same point—a closed tour—or begin and end at different points—an open tour. For a closed tour, every edge going into a node has to be matched by an edge leaving it. The number of edges joining to any given vertex has to be even (the valency of the node must be even). Looking at our network we can see that three of the nodes (A, B and C) have a valency of 3 and there is one of valency 5 (E). So a closed tour is impossible.

An open tour allows some nodes to have an odd valency—but only two: the node you start at and the node you end at. The Königsberg network has four nodes with odd valencies, so an open tour is also impossible.

Euler's major contribution was to go further than this one problem and generalize this to any network. The networks have to be connected—that is, you can get from any node to any other node by some path. In other words, the network is complete and connected. In such a network, having no more than two nodes is sufficient to ensure that there is an open or closed route through. You are probably familiar with a popular recreational math pastime that challenges you to trace a complete figure without lifting your pen off the paper or going over a line twice.

Paths and Circuits

Let's consider a network that has two nodes with odd valencies. The route through has to start and end at these nodes if we are to go along each edge just once. This is called an Eulerian path. Now let's try a network with two nodes and even valencies. Here, we have to start and end at the same node, then complete a Eulerian circuit.

Modern Applications

Like much of mathematics, Euler's study of networks and the field of graph theory were initially largely the result of just playing around with the mathematics for its own sake. There are now, however, many applications of graph theory. For example, graph theory is central in modern biology in reconstructing the genetic material RNA (a cousin to DNA) when only fragments are available. Eulerian paths provide the key to this reconstruction.

Profile

Leonhard Euler

Euler was a Swiss mathematician and physicist who introduced much of the mathematical notation and terminology that we use today.

He developed the ideas of Fermat in number theory, making progress on prime numbers and perfect numbers. He worked on graph theory, which is the basis of computer networks today, and solved the problem known as The Seven Bridges of Königsberg. He solved real-world problems with mathematical analysis and developed calculus so that it could be applied to physics. He also developed a logical tool for syllogistic reasoning, called Euler diagrams, similar to Venn diagrams. In geometry, Euler proved the existence of the Euler line. He developed a formula for polyhedra, which shows there is a constant relationship between the faces, edges and vertices of all polygons. He also produced a formula for dividing polygons into triangles with diagonals. He helped subsequent mathematicians understand pi with his improved formula to take it to more decimal places.

Euler was the most prolific mathematician of all time—he published 886 books.

The Life of Euler

Leonhard Euler (pronounced Oiler) was born in Basel in 1707. He studied widely in order to become a minister, like his father. However, the Swiss mathematician Bernoulli was his tutor, and Bernoulli encouraged Euler to become a mathematician. At the age of 20, Euler was appointed to the St. Petersburg Academy of Sciences as an academic. During his time in St. Petersburg, he worked on the science of the human voice, theories of sound and music, the mechanics of vision, and telescopic and microscopic perception.

He stayed until the political situation in Russia became too difficult. In 1741 he was offered a post at the Berlin Academy of Sciences by Frederick the Great of Prussia. He was there for 25 years, tutoring the king's children, and producing quantities of scientific papers, including substantial work on calculus.

Euler's eyesight became worse as he got older. He was nearly blind in one eye, and developed a cataract in the other. However, he worked on complex mathematical problems mentally and he had a photographic memory. He could recite the whole of Virgil's *Aeneid* by visualizing it on the page.

"Now I will have less distraction."

—Leonhard Euler, on losing sight in his right eye

CATALAN NUMBERS

Eugène Catalan (1814–1894) was a Belgian mathematician who defined what are now called the Catalan numbers. Catalan noticed a connection between the counting sequence for Euler's polygon division problem and moves in the Tower of Hanoi puzzle. There are many counting problems in combinatorics that result in the Catalan numbers: 1, 1, 2, 5, 14, 42, 132, 429 ...

Using brackets in a mathematical way produces the Catalan numbers. Each bracket has to be completed by another, while pairs of brackets can be contained within other pairs:

()

(())   ()()

(()())   ((()))   ()()()   (())()

()(())

Shaking hands across a circular table produces the Catalan numbers. How many ways can everyone shake hands with everyone else without crossing arms?

In 1766, Catherine the Great invited Euler back to Russia, and he lived there for the rest of his life. He and his wife had 13 children, five of whom survived childhood. He died in 1783.

Euler's Polygon Division Problem

In 1751, Euler posed a problem to fellow mathematician Christian Goldbach. The problem asks the question: in how many different ways can you divide a plane convex polygon into triangles by diagonals?

For a square, the answer is 2. For a pentagon, the answer is 5. For a hexagon, there are many more choices, giving 14 possibilities.

The number sequence starts: 1, 2, 5, 14, 42, 132..., so the numbers get large quickly. Euler painstakingly worked out the formula for determining these numbers.

• The diagram shows the systematic drawing of diagonals to divide these polygons into triangles. For a heptagon, there are 42 different ways; for an octagon, 132.

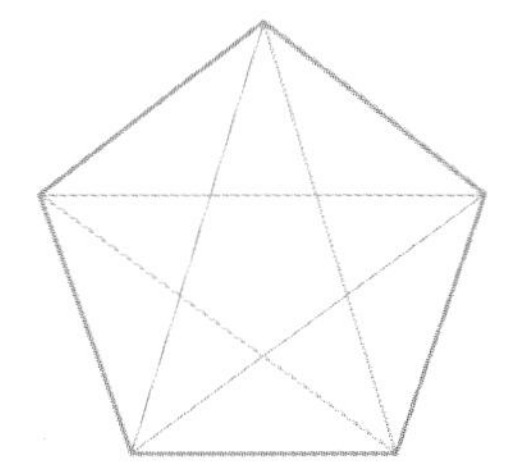

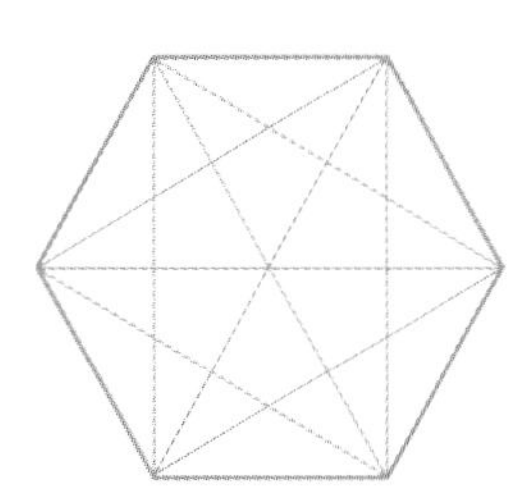

Exercise 23

Mutual Friends

THE PROBLEM:

Bubbles is the perfect hostess. When throwing a party, she likes to make sure that there are at least three people there who know each other. Or failing that, at least three people who do not know each other (so that she can introduce them to each other). What is the smallest number of people that Bubbles has to invite to ensure that one or other of these conditions occurs?

THE METHOD:

Graph theory provides the means of reasoning out a solution here, by representing party guests as nodes and the connections between them as edges. We start by looking at a small number, say five guests. It is possible to seat five guests around a table so that each guest knows the person to their left or right but no one else.

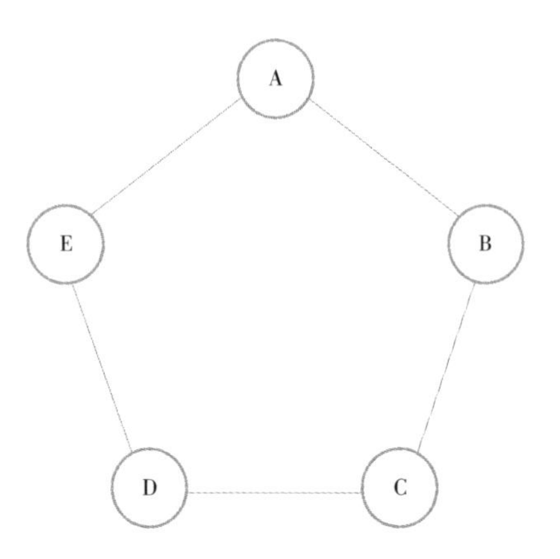

We can see from this that there is no trio of mutual friends, as there is no triangle formed in the network. Is there a trio of mutual strangers? We can draw a complementary network linking people to those that they do not know.

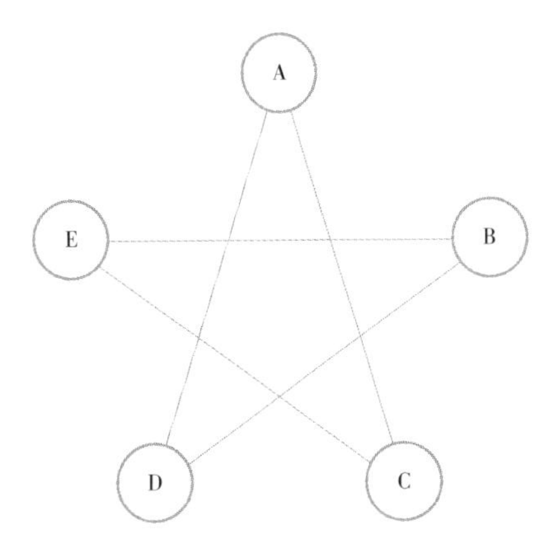

Again, there is no triangle formed, so there is not a group of three mutual strangers.

What about six guests? Rather then draw the entire network we concentrate on one guest, say Agatha. Agatha must either know at least three of the other five guests, or is a stranger to at least three other guests. Let's start with the first possibility, that Agatha (A) knows at least three others (if she knows more than three it does not matter, we only need to consider at least three). Beginning the network for Agatha and her three friends is simple.

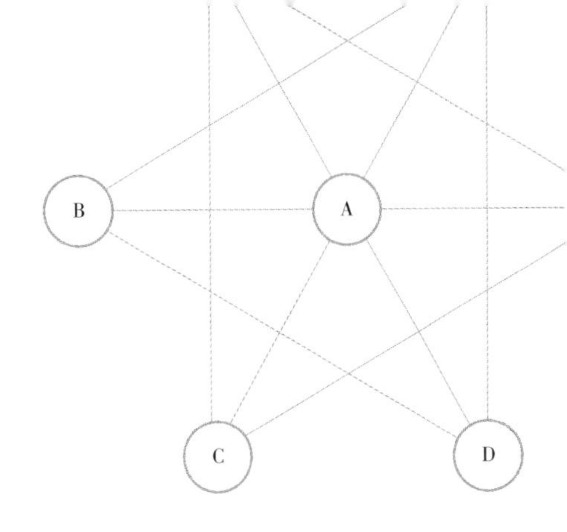

If those three friends of Agatha's do not know each other, then we have found our triple of three mutual strangers. If two of them do know each other then we have found a trio of mutual friends.

So if Agatha knows at least three people out of the five we are certain of finding either three mutual friends or three mutual strangers.

If Agatha does not know at least three other people, and if two out of that three do not know each other, then those two together with Agatha are three mutual strangers. The only way for this not to happen is for these three people to all know each other, in which case we have found our triple of mutual friends.

THE SOLUTION:

As long as Bubbles invites at least six people to her party, she is certain to have a group of three mutual friends or three mutual strangers. Cheers.

FOUR-COLOR PROBLEM

In 1852, Francis Guthrie, a mathematics student, became intrigued by the number of colors needed to color a map so that no two adjacent regions shared the same color. Whatever configuration he tried, Guthrie could not find a map that needed more than four colors. But neither he, nor his tutor, the logician, De Morgan could prove it. So simple to set up and understand, this "four-color problem" stumped mathematicians for over a century.

Badge-making

Suppose a badgemaker wants to have the designs below printed up. She wants to use the minimum number of colors on each. How many colors are needed for each badge, so that no two adjacent regions are the same color? By adjacent we mean sharing a common side; regions sharing only a common point may be the same color.

The first badge needs only two colors: regions diagonally opposite each other can be colored the same. The second badge, although it has fewer regions, actually requires three colors, while the third badge needs four. Try as you might, you will never design a badge that needs five colors. This is the essence of the four-color conjecture: that a maximum of four colors are needed to color any map and not have adjacent regions the same color.

Complexity in Simplicity

Setting up the four-color conjecture is simple, but establishing the truth of it proved quite intractable. While no one has ever been able to draw a map that could not be colored with four colors, that is not enough to convince the sceptical mathematician that somewhere, over the horizon, there may be a map lurking that does require more than four colors.

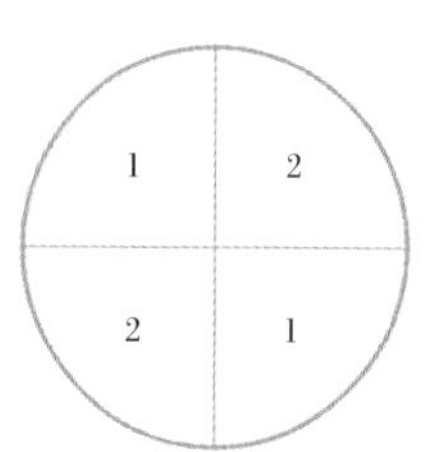

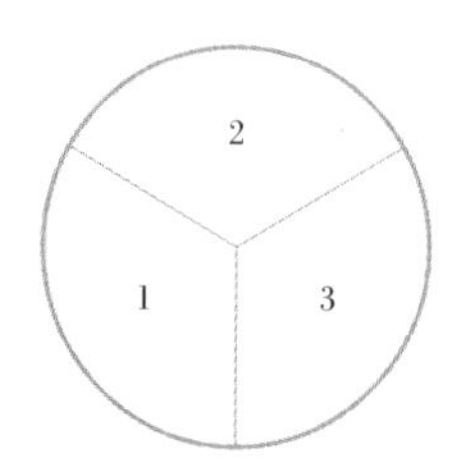

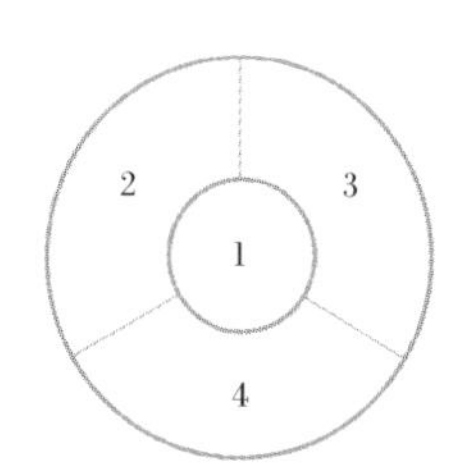

A Slow Acceptance

Perhaps the seemingly simple nature of the problem put mathematicians off serious study of it. Maybe they thought that such a simple problem must have a simple proof and any mathematician who published on the problem would appear foolish if the simple solution did subsequently emerge. The first article on the problem in 1860 was published anonymously, and although the mathematician Cayley wrote about it in 1879, this was for the Royal Geographical Society. A proof by Kempe was also published in 1879, but shown to be flawed in 1890 by Heawood. And there things got stuck until 1976. That was when Appel and Haken produced a proof that involved using a computer to check over 1000 cases. A subsequent proof in 1996 used fewer than 500 cases, but still required a computer. Mathematicians hotly debated whether or not such approaches constitute a proper "proof" at the time although it has gained more acceptance now.

From Four to Seven Colors

The four-color conjecture holds true for plane (flat) maps and it also holds true for maps drawn on the surface of a sphere or cylinder or any similar solid. But what about a map drawn on something shaped like a doughnut or lifesaver—a torus, to give it its mathematical name? Well, it is possible to create a map that requires seven colors if no adjacent regions are to be the same color. The figures below show how a map colored in seven colors can be transformed into a torus with every region then adjoining every other region.

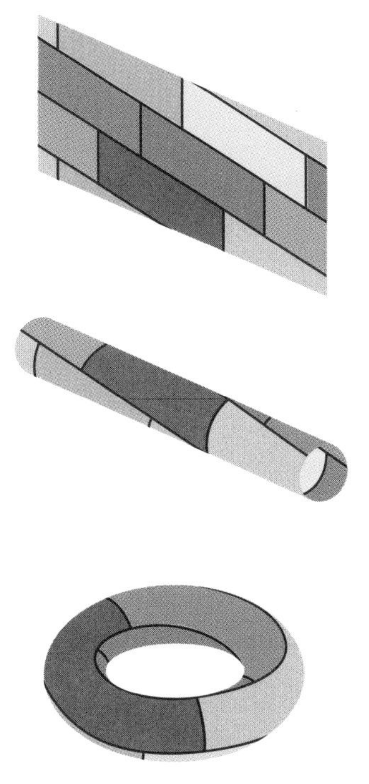

"Suppose there's a brown calf and a big brown dog, and an artist is making a picture of them. . . He has got to paint them so you can tell them apart the minute you look at them, hain't he. . . It's just the same with maps. That's why they make every state a different color."

—Mark Twain

Exercise 24 Five-color Problem

THE PROBLEM:

It has proved difficult to show that no map requires more than four colors. Can we establish that it is impossible to create a map of five regions that needs five colors for adjacent regions to be different colors?

THE METHOD:

The approach here is to turn the problem into an equivalent network problem. Any map can be turned into a "dual" network. In the dual, we represent the regions by vertices; if the regions are adjacent then the two vertices are joined by an edge. Here is a map and its dual.

One key feature of the networks that are created in this way is that they are "planar"; that is, they can always be drawn so that none of the edges cross each other.

Our problem can now be restated. Is it possible to construct a planar graph with five vertices where each vertex is joined to every other vertex? If we can do this then the dual map of the network would need five colors.

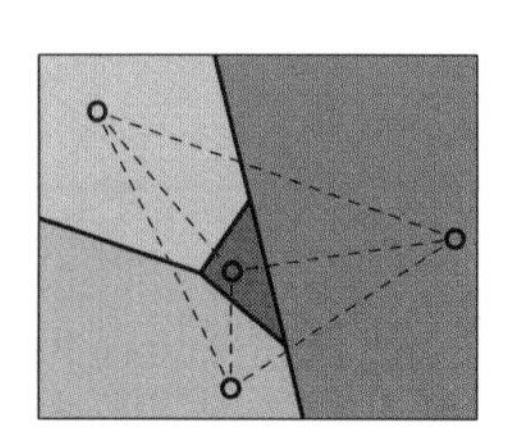

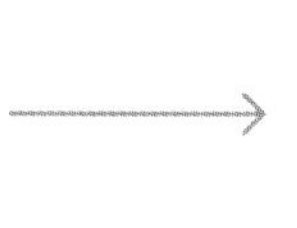

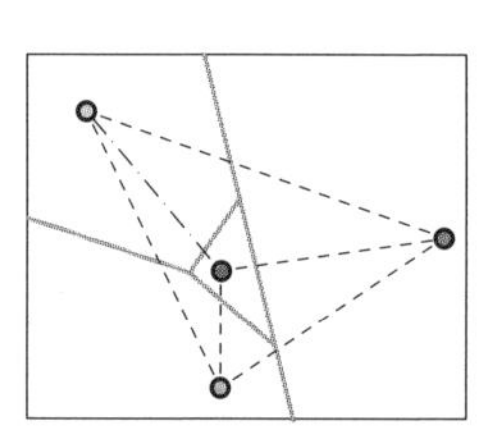

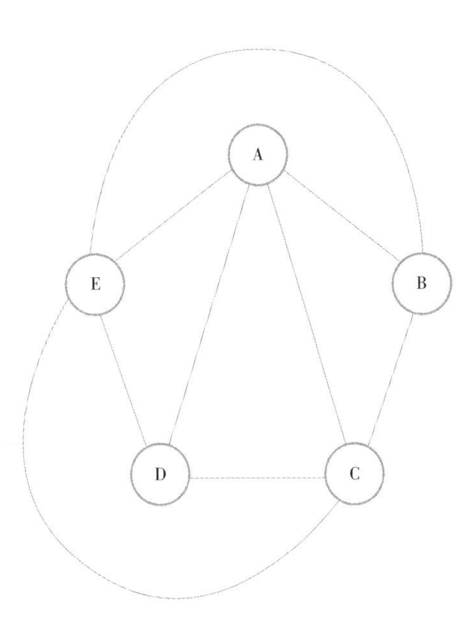

For clarity, let's arrange our five nodes at the corners of a pentagon and fill in some initial edges.

We can join node A to the other two nodes inside the pentagon and node B to the other two nodes outside the pentagon.

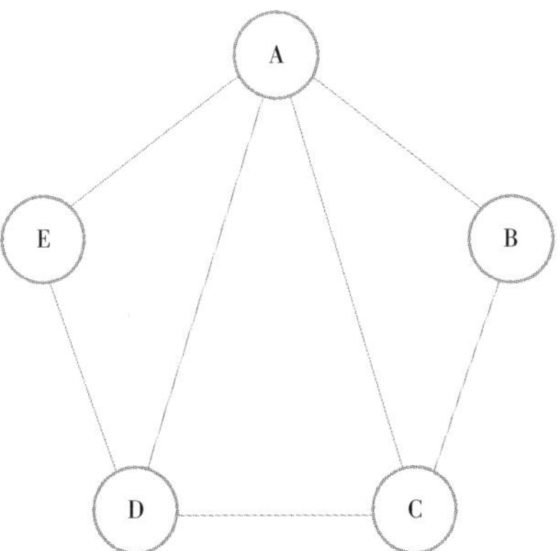

But we cannot join C to D inside the pentagon without crossing one of the edges, nor can we join C to D outside the pentagon without crossing one of the edges. If we do cross an edge, then our network is no longer planar and so is not a dual of a map. We can thus conclude that since it is impossible to construct a five-node planar network where every node is connected to every other node, it is also impossible to construct a map that needs five colors.

THE SOLUTION:

We have shown that five regions cannot be drawn in the plane so that each of them is adjacent to every other. Sadly, this in itself does not establish the truth of the four-color conjecture: it may still be possible to create a map with lots of regions where the interactions between collections of regions do mean that four colors are not enough.

Profile

Paul Erdös

Paul Erdös (pronounced AIR-dosh) was a prolific and eccentric Hungarian mathematician. He published more papers than any other mathematician in history, and collaborated with hundreds of others. He was so highly regarded that it was an honor to be associated with him, and a system of "Erdös numbers" arose. To earn Erdös Number 1, you collaborated directly with him; Erdös Number 2, with someone who worked directly with him; and so on. There are 4,500 Erdös Number 2 collaborators, and about 200,000 mathematicians have been assigned an Erdös number.

Erdös worked on a wide range of mathematics, including number theory, combinatorics, graph theory, and set theory, and he developed a new area, discrete mathematics, which is the basis of computer science.

The Life of Erdös

Paul Erdös was born in 1913 in Budapest in Hungary to Jewish parents, and was a child prodigy—he discovered negative numbers at the age of three. His two older sisters died of scarlet fever and as a consequence Erdös had a very protected childhood—he did not tie his own shoelaces before he was 14 or prepare any food for himself until he was 21. His parents were both mathematics teachers, and they tutored him at home. His father, as a prisoner of war during the First World War, taught himself English. He did not know any English speakers, so his pronunciation was odd—and when he returned he taught the language to Paul, who spoke it with the same strange accent for the rest of his life.

Erdös received a doctorate from the University of Budapest at the age of 20. He had discovered an elegant proof for Chebyshev's theorem, which states that for each number greater than one, there is always at least one prime number between it and its double. Because of anti-semitism in Hungary, Erdös moved to the University of Manchester in the UK. He continued to travel and move around all his life, unable to return to Hungary to live. He took up temporary posts in the USA, but during the McCarthy period he was refused entry to the USA, and was not allowed back until 1963.

Traveling Mathematician

Erdös lived from a suitcase and had no property—he said "property is a nuisance." He traveled from conference to conference and campus to campus throughout the world, staying with other mathematicians, and living on coffee and caffeine tablets. The mathematician Stan Ulam said of him: "His peculiarities are so numerous it is impossible to describe them all."

His mother traveled with him until she died in 1971. The American mathematician Ron

Graham provided a permanent room for Erdös, and managed all his finances and everyday living problems. Erdös gave all his money away as bursaries or prizes or to charitable causes. Throughout his life he offered prizes, small and large, for solutions to unresolved problems, and these are still offered from his estate. Erdös never married, was not interested in relationships, and had no children. He said people who were married were "captured," and found physical contact repellent. He died of a heart attack in 1996, aged 83, while working on an equation at a conference in Warsaw.

ERDÖS' PROBLEMS

During his life, Erdös set countless problems for other mathematicians to tackle, and he collaborated with hundreds of people on exploring these problems. Many of the problems could be solved by keen undergraduate students. Many of his problems were on graph theory, exploring networks of connections. One example is the Erdös–Faber–Lovász conjecture (1972), a problem about what is called the coloring of graphs, which developed from the four-color problem (see pp. 136–137). The conjecture arose from a problem about assigning seating for a series of university committees, and poses the problem: is it possible for each committee member to sit in the same chair for all the different committees they are on?

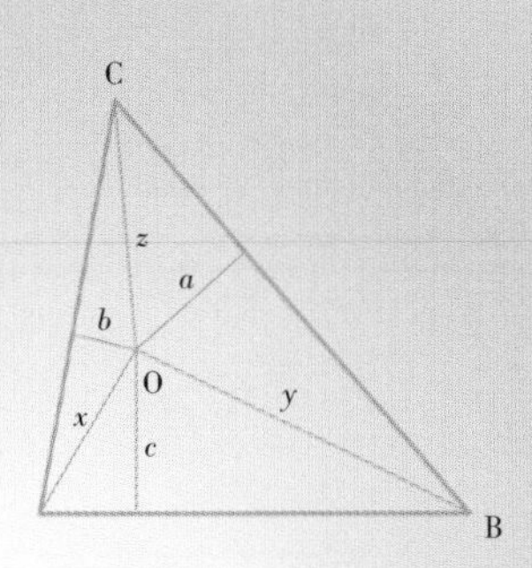

• Erdös set this as a problem to be proved: the sum of the distances from O to the sides is less than or equal to half of the sum of the distances from O to the vertices. It was proved by Louis Mordell in 1937.

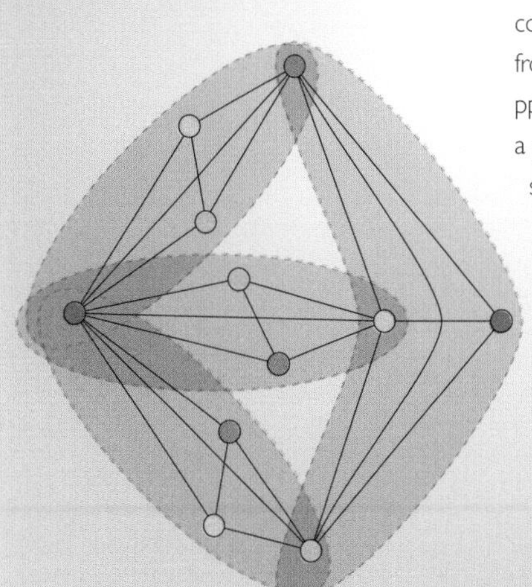

• An instance of the Erdös–Faber–Lovász conjecture: four cliques of four vertices each, any two of which intersect in a single vertex, can be four-colored.

PROJECTIVE GEOMETRY

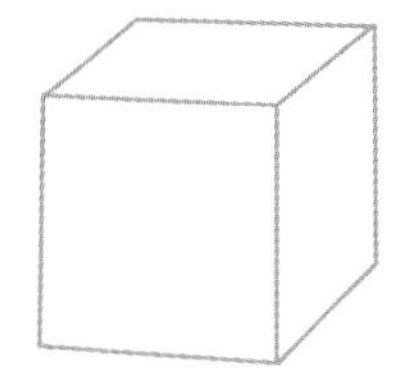

What object is this?

Go to the bottom of the class if you think it's a cube (don't worry, you'll be joining nearly everyone else). It is, of course a hexagon. Cubes are three-dimensional and this is a two-dimensional representation. We happily go about "seeing" two-dimensional objects as though they were solid. Representing three-dimensional objects in two dimensions was not addressed mathematically until the mid-17th century.

Tricks of Perspective

Italian Renaissance artists were interested in how to represent the glories of the world through two-dimensional paintings, and the Italian artist and architect Leon Battista Alberti was one of the founders of the mathematics of "projective geometry"—creating the image resulting from shapes projected onto a screen. Alberti's first "trick" was to use only one eye for painting. The fact that our eyes are set slightly apart means that each eye receives a marginally different image of the world; the brain assembles these to create a sense of three-dimensionality and the ability to judge distances. Closing one eye shuts out this stereoscopic vision and "flattens" our perception of the world. Modern 3D movies reverse this process. The glasses make sure each eye sees slightly different versions of a flat image, fooling the brain to thinking these are coming from 3D objects.

Alberti's second trick was to put a plane between himself and the world he was painting. This screen was a sheet of glass with points marked on it. By matching up the real world to the points and drawing directly onto the glass, the projection created was an accurate representation of the scene. Later he used a trellis "veil" of threads to look through in the vertical plane and match up the corresponding points on a grid drawn on a horizontal canvas.

In 1636, the French mathematician Girard Desargues published a paper that set out geometrical methods for constructing projections of objects. In this paper he analyzed perspective drawings and identified which elements of the three-dimensional world are preserved in them. In a perspective drawing, points, lines, and planes are preserved because they are usually represented as points, lines, and planes. Angles, lengths, and the relationships between lengths, however, usually change. The most striking difference is the way in which parallel lines meet.

Not all parallel lines meet in a classic projection. Those moving away from the viewer meet at a "vanishing point." Parallel lines running across the field of vision remain parallel but get closer together toward the vanishing point: a property they may not have in the real world.

Take for example, a chess board. How can we represent this accurately in projective geometry?

Alberti had a neat solution to this.

• Draw the "vertical" lines of the board first, spacing them equally apart at the bottom of the page and meeting at a vanishing point.

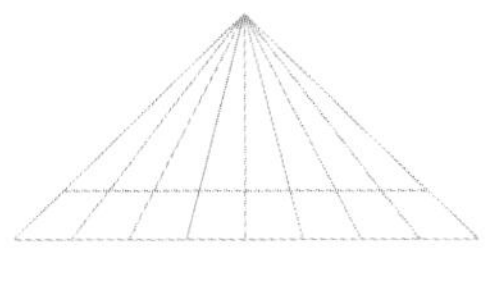

• Draw in the first pair of horizontal lines.

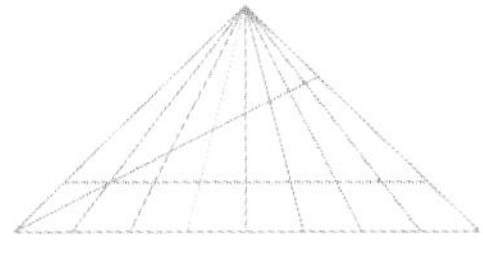

• Now draw a diagonal through the bottom left-hand square and extend it toward the vanishing point.

• Draw the other horizontal lines at the points of intersection between this diagonal line and the other "verticals."

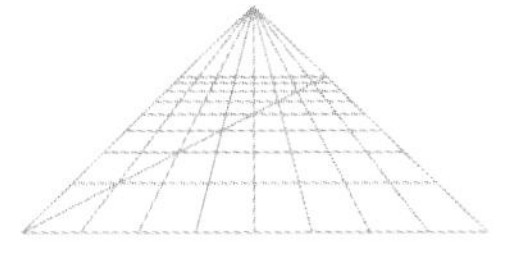

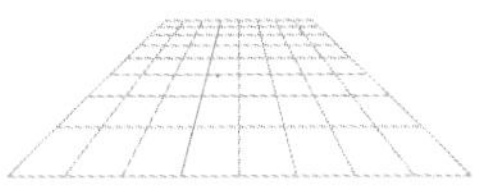

PAPPUS' HEXAGON THEOREM

Imagine two rows of three olive trees. The three trees in each row are in a straight line but these lines are not parallel to each other. Can you plant three more olive trees in a straight line between these two lines so that ten rows of three trees are created?

This problem can be solved using Pappus' hexagon theorem. This states that if you join any three points on a straight line to three points on a second lines, irrespective of the spacing of the points along the line, the three points of intersection created will always lie on a straight line.

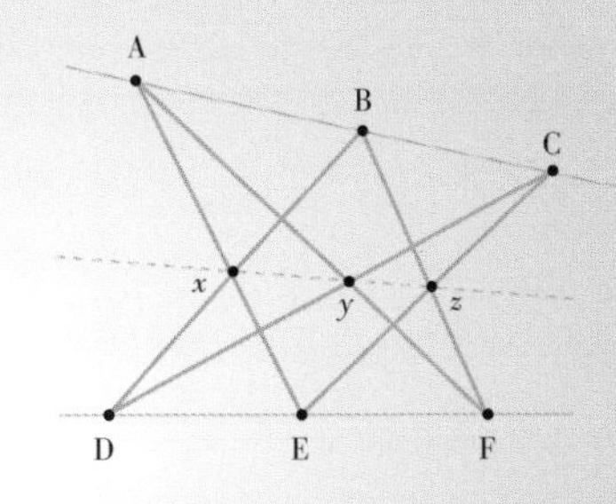

The farmer can solve his olive tree problem by transplanting tree B along the line it is on so that BYE forms the tenth straight line.

Established in around 340, Pappus' hexagon theorem is significant in that it does not draw on any measurements and is thus considered to be the first example of projective geometry.

MERCATOR

Picture a tennis ball within its cylindrical container sitting on a table. We can imagine planes slicing horizontally through the cylinder and the ball. Where the plane meets the ball, we can project the image of the surface of the ball onto the cylinder. Slice open the cylinder with a vertical cut and we get a flat projection of the ball onto the plane. In this way it is possible to make a map of the globe.

A Flat Earth

We can create a similar projected map of Earth by imagining the planet in a huge cylinder. We project out horizontally from each point on the globe to the corresponding point on the cylinder. We then slice the cylinder open—by convention, we do this at the line of longitude lying 180° east. This produces an interesting picture of the world: a regular cylindrical or normal aspect orientation.

This doesn't look like the map of the globe with which we are more familiar. Antarctica looks very odd spread out along the entire bottom edge of the map. The most unfamiliar feature of this map is that it presents both the lines of latitude and longitude as parallel. Unfamiliar though it is, could this have been the map we might have adopted? Maps are only as good as the use they can be put to, so could this map be used for navigation?

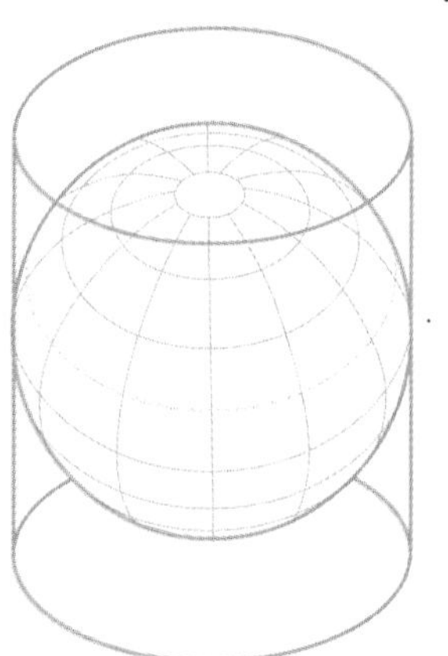

• The Alsatian mathematician Johann Heinrich Lambert developed the Lambert cylindrical equal-area projection in 1772.

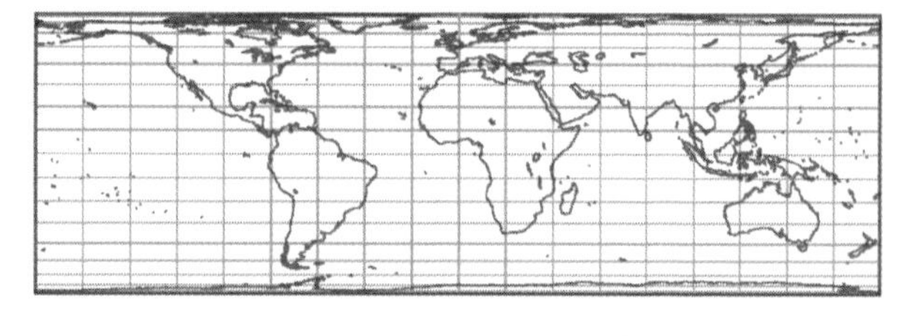

• 160° west is the central meridian on the Lambert cylindrical projection, focusing the map on the oceans.

We saw earlier (see pp. 92–93) that the shortest distance between two points on a globe is to follow an arc of a great circle. Joining up, say New York and Rome on this cylindrical projection map does not follow a great circle, nor does it even follow the rhumb line that sailors had previously followed. This difficulty arises because this projection alters angles. We need a map that preserves angles—a "conformal projection," to give it its mathematical name. Joining points on such a projection still does not give an arc of a great circle, but it does show the rhumb line.

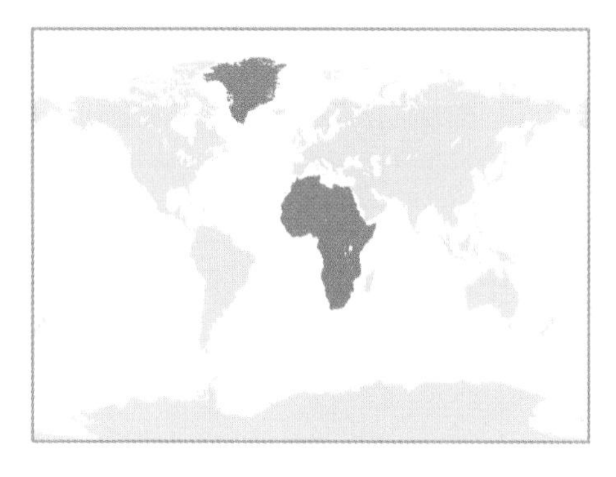

• In the Mercator projection, we get a distorted view, as Greenland appears to be as large as Africa.

Mercator Map

The familiar Mercator map has this property of being conformal—straight lines on the map are rhumb lines. Although often referred to as the Mercator projection, the map is not actually a projection in the mathematical sense of the word: the map cannot be produced by imagining the globe in a cylinder and drawing lines from the globe to project points onto the cylinder.

We are so familiar with the Mercator map that we may fail to appreciate that it too presents a somewhat distorted view of the world. As we move away from the equator, areas increase disproportionately. Greenland is nothing like the size of Africa, as it appears to be on the map. Incidentally, Mercator also introduced the use of the word "atlas."

Gnomonic Map

Are there projections of the globe where straight lines are indeed great circles? Yes. The gnomonic map does this, although it is more of a curiosity than having any real practical purpose.

• The shortest route between two locations in reality corresponds to that on a gnomonic map.

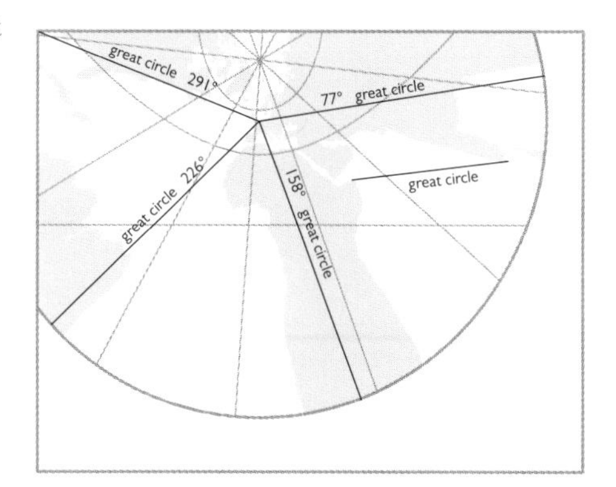

Profile Bernhard Riemann

Riemann was a German mathematician who had a significant influence on mathematical thinking, in particular in two areas: non-Euclidean geometry and prime numbers. His ideas on differential geometry were developed by the Italian school of mathematicians, Beltrami, Ricci, and Levi-Civita. Later, their worked was used by Einstein for general relativity.

The Life of Riemann

Bernhard Riemann was born in 1826 in the Kingdom of Hanover, now in Germany. He was taught by his father, a Lutheran minister, until he was ten years old and he showed such an aptitude for mathematics that his father employed a tutor. At school, Riemann studied with the intention of becoming a minister, but mathematics absorbed him. Recognizing his interest, the director of the high school lent Riemann a textbook by the mathematician Legendre on number theory. Six days later Riemann returned the 859-page book, saying what a wonderful book it was and that he now knew it by heart. He was very shy and found it difficult to make friends.

Riemann's father allowed him to study mathematics rather than theology at the University of Göttingen. There he attended the lectures of Gauss. After a year he moved to Berlin to study with Eisenstein, Dirichlet, and other brilliant mathematicians, who influenced him profoundly.

He returned to Göttingen after two years to complete his PhD under Gauss. In order to qualify as a lecturer and to charge students fees, Riemann had to deliver a keynote lecture. Gauss gave him the subject of the foundations of geometry. Riemann was a hypochondriac, shy, prone to depression, and hidden behind a full black beard. He was studying physics as well as mathematics, and the pressures of the work nearly caused a breakdown. But, influenced by his work on physics, he gave a brilliant lecture in 1854, which caused a shift in the way geometry was understood. The key idea behind Riemann's theory was the curvature of space, extending into non-Euclidean geometry; this led into Einstein's revolutionary ideas half a century later.

Riemann became professor of mathematics in 1859. He was now working on prime numbers, and published a paper on what is now called the Riemann hypothesis. Once again, his ideas had a profound influence on mathematical thinking. He married in 1862, but died of tuberculosis the following year, aged 39. After his death, a tidy housekeeper destroyed many of his papers until Riemann's family intervened. We do not know what treasures may have been lost forever.

rofile

Georg Pick

Pick was an Austrian mathematician. He is known for what is called Pick's theorem, which is a formula for determining the area of lattice polygons.

The Life of Pick

Georg Pick was born in 1859 in Vienna to a Jewish family. He was educated at home by his father until the age of 11, then went to school. He studied mathematics and physics at the University of Vienna, and published a mathematics paper when he was 17. He was awarded a PhD at 21, and was appointed as a lecturer in Prague the following year. Except for one year studying under Klein at the University of Leipzig, Pick remained in Prague. He became a professor at the German University of Prague in 1892.

In 1910 he was on the university committee set up to consider appointing Einstein to the university. Pick argued strongly for his appointment and Einstein was made chair of mathematical physics in 1911. The two became good friends and both shared a passion for music. Pick was a good violinist and played in a quartet consisting of four professors from the university.

When he retired in 1927, Pick moved back to Vienna, but in 1938, when German troops marched into Austria he returned to Prague. The Nazis subsequently occupied Prague, and at the age of 82 Pick was sent to Theresienstadt concentration camp, where he died two weeks later.

"Pick was a bachelor and uncommonly correct in clothes and attitude."—***Anonymous***

Pick's Work

Pick's mathematical work was broad and he published 67 papers ranging across many topics such as linear algebra, invariant theory, integral calculus, potential theory, functional analysis, and geometry. More than half of his papers were on functions of a complex variable, differential equations and differential geometry.

Pick's theorem provides a link between traditional Euclidean geometry and modern digital discrete geometry. Pick published his paper on the theorem in 1899, but it did not receive wide attention until 1969 in a book by Hugo Steinhaus called *Mathematical Snapshots*.

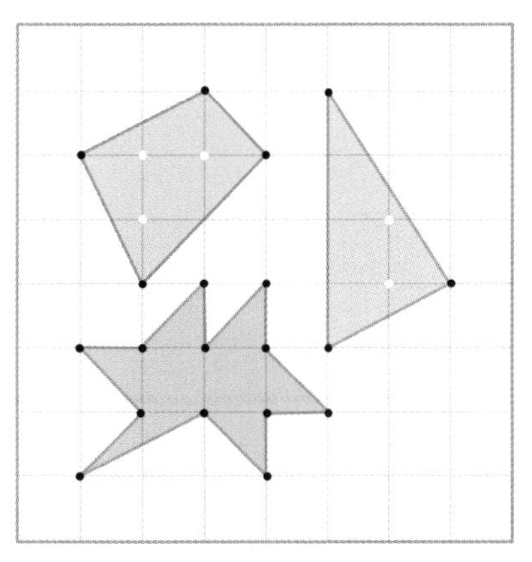

• Simply stated, Pick's theorem for finding the area of a simple polygon on a grid is: (1) count the dots on the perimeter of the polygon; (2) divide the number by 2; (3) subtract 1; (4) add the interior dots.

Pick's Theorem

THE PROBLEM:

Fabio has inherited a piece of land from his brother. He has a map of the area and some tracing paper printed with a square grid. How can Fabio quickly estimate the area of the land?

THE METHOD:

One obvious way is to place the tracing paper over the map, trace the outline of the plot of land and count up the squares. Part squares need to be estimated as to whether or not they are more or less than half a square; those part squares less than a whole square are counted as one, those less than half a square are discarded.

Using this method, Fabio gets an estimate for the area of 23 square units. (Whatever the size of the squares on the grid, these can be scaled up using the scale on the map.)

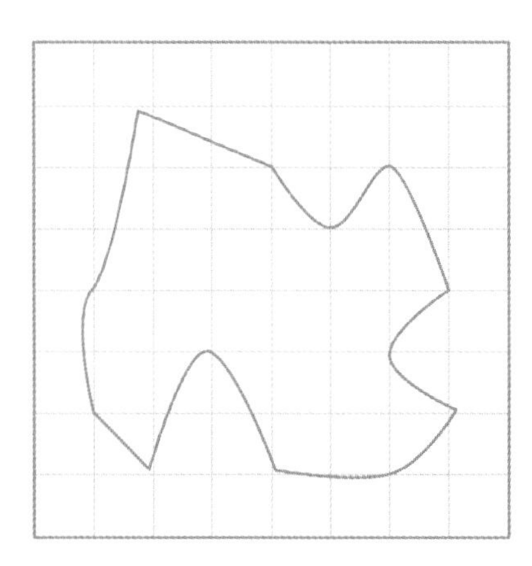

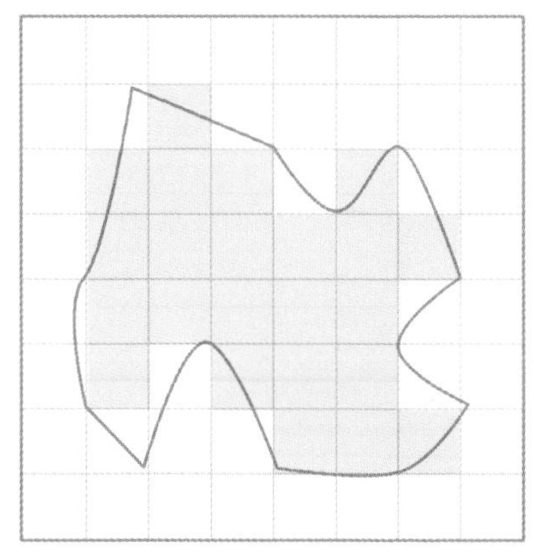

But there is a quicker method that Fabio can also use. This time he focuses on the intersection points on the grid, rather than on the squares. Drawing on the grid, Fabio creates an approximation to the plot of land by joining up grid points with straight lines.

Instead of counting up squares, Fabio now counts up grid points. First he counts the number of points actually on the perimeter of the polygon he drew (the black points)—the boundary points. Then he counts the number of points enclosed within the polygon—the interior points (yellow in the diagram).

The area of the polygon is given by the formula:

$$A = \frac{1}{2}B + I - 1$$

For Fabio's field, B = 13, I = 18, so the area is $\frac{1}{2}$ 13 + 18 − 1 = 23.5 square units.

THE SOLUTION:

A simple way to find areas is to create a "lattice polygon," one whose vertices lie on the points of a square lattice. The area is given by the formula:

$$A = \frac{1}{2}B + I - 1$$

where B is the number of boundary points and I is the number of interior points.

The result is "Pick's theorem," named after Georg Pick, who proved it in 1899. It works for all lattice polygons, as long as there is not a hole in the polygon. Since the result rests on simple counting of discrete points (rather than continuous lengths), Pick's theorem is significant for linking traditional Euclidean geometry with modern discrete geometry.

• = 13 perimeter points (B)

• = 18 interior points (I)

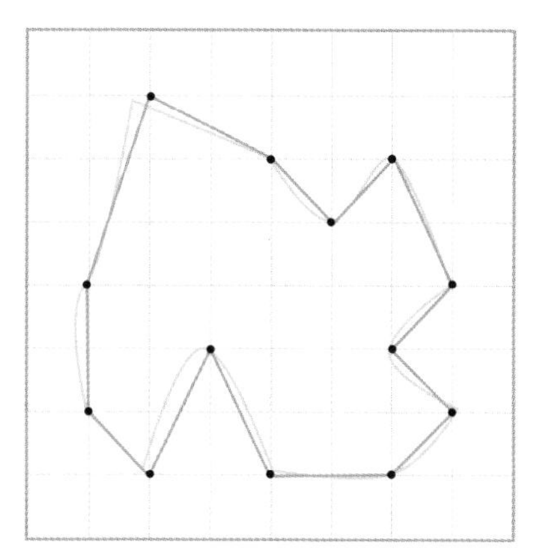

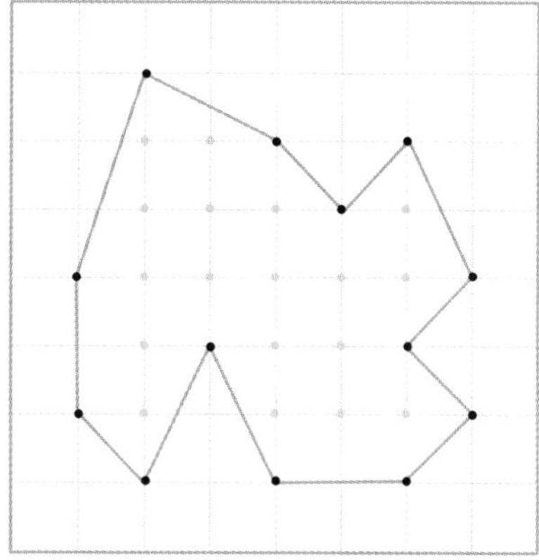

Chapter

6

Bottles, Donuts, and Coastlines

The mathematical world of squares, cubes, ellipses, and so forth all assume that such geometrical objects have smooth edges. But the world we actually live in is much bumpier, more wrinkled, and holier (in the literal sense) than these idealized mathematical objects. As mathematicians began to question whether classical geometry had very much at all to do with the real world, so new geometries emerged that accepted the rough edges of the world.

ONE SIDE ONLY

Mathematics is not famous for its jokes, but one goes: how many different types of mathematicians are there? Three; those who can count and those who cannot. Not a joke, the answer to the question, How many sides does a piece of paper have? was considered self-evidently to be two. Until along came Augustus Möbius, famous for his (mathematical) band.

The properties of the Möbius band are really best appreciated by playing with paper, so unless you are reading this in bed we encourage you to grab a sheet of paper and cut it into five or six strips lengthways (so you have a collection of strips of paper about the width of your thumb and long enough to join to make a loop).

To make a cylindrical band, simply take a strip of paper and glue the ends together.

Hold this band so that you can draw a line along the center of the paper (easiest to put the paper and pen on a flat surface and move the paper rather than the pen) and, unsurprisingly, the line you draw will meet up to form a closed loop. Inspect the cylindrical band and you'll see that the line is on one side of the paper and the other side is blank. No surprises there.

To make a Möbius band, take a strip of paper and, before gluing the ends together, give one of the ends a half, 180°, twist.

Draw a line along the center of this band and, as before, it will join up with itself. But look closely at the Möbius band and you will see that you have drawn the line both inside and outside the band. A Möbius band only has one side. Of course, you twisted the paper before joining the ends, so this may seem obvious, but before mathematicians like Möbius started exploring this idea, mathematicians did not appreciate the difference between objects with two surfaces and those with only one. What is surprising is that there is no record of exploring the properties of one-sided shapes until the mid-1800s. Such study is now a central part of the branch of geometry known as topology.

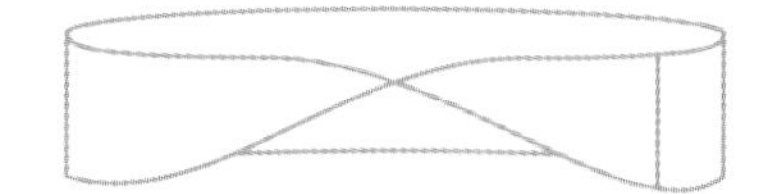

Klein Bottle

A one-sided Möbius band can actually exist in the real world. In 1882, the German mathematician Felix Klein extended the idea of one-sidedness further. He imagined a bottle with a neck that wraps back into the bottle. However, strictly speaking, a Klein bottle can only really exist in four dimensions. Just as we cannot distinguish one side from the other on a Möbius band, so a Klein bottle has no separation from inside and outside. You can paint the outside of a cola bottle without painting the inside. Paint a Klein bottle and the entire surface gets covered.

Playing with Möbius

The Möbius band has some other quirky properties worth exploring (and at one time the mainstay of magicians). Imagine following these instructions with a simple cylindrical band and your intuitions of how things turn out are likely to be quite accurate. Things aren't at all obvious with a Möbius band.
Cut your Möbius band along the pencil line you drew along it. A cylinder will give you two separate bands but does a Möbius band give you two separate bands?

Cut the Möbius band in a similar way but start the cut one third of the way in from the edge, rather than the center. A cylinder will give you two bands, one wider than the other. A Möbius band will give you a surprising result.

Finally you might like to explore all of this with another band. Make a full, 360° twist before joining the ends together.

MÖBIUS

Augustus Möbius was a German mathematician and theoretical astronomer. He is best known for his discovery of the Möbius strip, which he published in a paper when he was 75. Although he is famous for his work in mathematics, he also published important work on astronomy.

Möbius was born in Saxony in 1790. He was a descendant of Martin Luther, from his mother's side. His mother died when he was three and he was educated at home until he was 13, when he went to college. He showed an early interest in mathematics and, at the University of Leipzig, studied mathematics, physics, and astronomy. In 1813 he traveled to Göttingen to study astronomy under Gauss.

He was appointed professor of astronomy and higher mechanics at the University of Leipzig in 1816 at the young age of 26. He was not a good lecturer and did not do well enough either to persuade students to pay for his lectures or to gain promotion. However, he did well as a researcher and eventually, in 1844, he was given a full professorship at the university. In 1848 he became director of the Observatory at Leipzig. He married and had three children. He died in Leipzig in 1868 at the age of 78.

Exercise 26

Linking Rings

THE PROBLEM:

Nana was left a Greek wedding ring by her grandmother. This consists of three gold bands linked together. Playing with the ring, Nana noticed that if one of the three bands was cut, the other two would still be linked together. She wondered if there is a way of linking the three rings so that if any one of the rings were cut, all three would separate. In fact, how many different ways are there of linking the three rings together?

THE METHOD:

Although it does not show how the rings relate to each other in terms of over- or underlapping, the linking of the three rings looks like this:

We can see that there are six vertices where the circles intersect with each other. At each of these six vertices one circle must pass under or over the other. Because there are two choices for each crossing, there are $2^6 = 64$ possible interlaced patterns.

However, not all of these patterns are different from each other. Two patterns are the same if you can get from one to the other by some transformation. There are three ways in which one arrangement can be turned into another: rotating a design through 120°; reflecting in a mirror line; and flipping a design over. If we remove the duplicates, we can reduce these 64 designs to only ten geometrically distinct patterns.

If we make up these ten designs into wedding rings, not all of them will result in the rings being linked. For example, one of the designs is simply the three rings laid on top of each other—pick them up and they are all separate.

Three of the ten give you two linked rings and a separate ring. Here is one of the three:

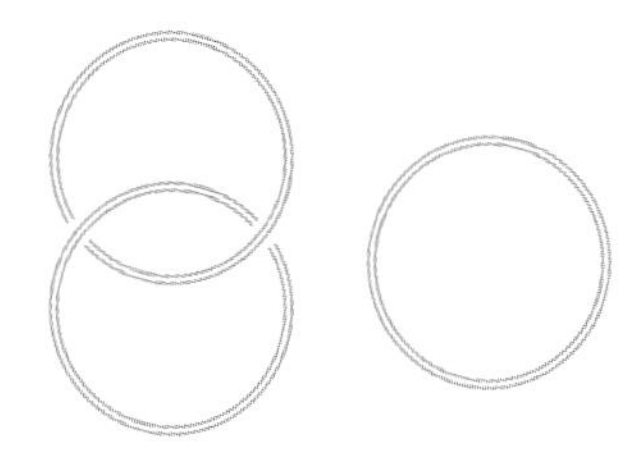

Three other arrangements result in a chain of three.

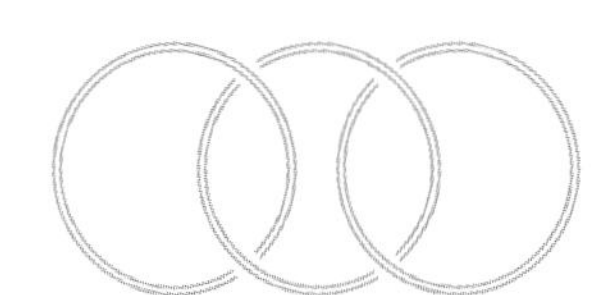

The remaining three designs link all three rings to each of the other two.

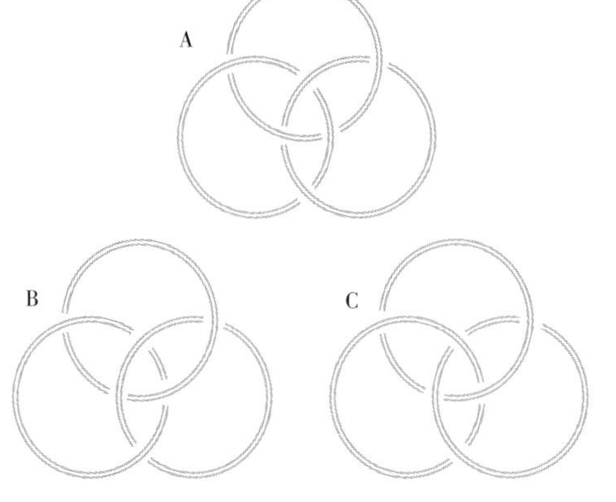

Only one of these three designs allows us to break any one of the three rings to unlink them all (see below).

THE SOLUTION:

It is possible to link three rings together in such a way that all three are interlinked but no two of the three are. This particular arrangement is known as the Borromean rings, named after an Italian Renaissance family who adopted it as their family emblem. The Borromeo palazzo on Isola Bella, Lake Maggiore, Italy is liberally decorated with this design and some of the variations above.

TOPOLOGY

To us plain folk, a teacup and a ring donut are as different as the proverbial chalk and cheese. But to the mathematician interested in the branch of geometry known as topology, a teacup and a ring donut are mathematically equivalent, as indeed are a stick of chalk and a cube of cheese.

Rubber Sheet Geometry

Topology is affectionately called the geometry of rubber sheets because it is a study of the properties of surfaces. In particular, topology concerns the properties of shapes that do not change (invariant) as shapes are transformed into other shapes. These transformations allow the shape to be stretched and pulled—topologists are not interested in size or angles.

Imagine a balloon partially inflated. It can be molded to resemble a football and, by pressing your fist into it, it can temporarily be made to resemble a bowl (containing a fist). Now, a game of football with Grandma's cut-glass bowl would not please anyone very much, but bowls and balls are topologically equivalent to each other. One can be transformed into the other. Indeed, the five Platonic solids (see pp. 76–77) are equivalent in the world of topology to a ball: a (mathematically) hollow rubber cube can be transformed into a ball, a tetrahedron or a flag-pole. In all these cases, the topologist is really only referring to the surface of the object being transformed.

Our balloon cannot, however, be transformed into something resembling a donut, at least not without puncturing the surface. Donuts are not topologically equivalent to balls because they have a hole in them. But a teacup is topologically the same as a donut—the hole occupies the place of the handle. A "rubber sheet" donut can be transformed into a teacup (theoretically!).

Torus

The mathematical name for donut-like shapes is a "torus." Two surfaces are regarded as being of the same type, topologically, if one can be continuously transformed into the other. The important thing here is "continuously." A torus can be continuously transformed into something resembling a cup. A ball cannot be continuously transformed into a torus: the surface needs puncturing at some point in order to create the hole for the handle.

A sphere has no holes, a torus one hole, and we can carry on adding holes to create a two-holed torus, three-holed and so forth. Every surface that is finite and has two sides (so it's not a Möbius band) turns out to be topologically equivalent to either a sphere or a torus with a finite number of holes.

We can appreciate this by thinking about closed loops on the surface of our object. Any loop around a ball can be continuously shrunk until it is reduced to a point.

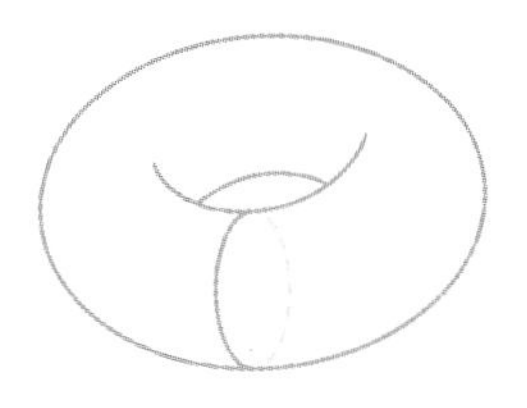

A loop on a torus that goes through the hole does not have this property: the loop cannot be continuously shrunk to a point, without either breaking the loop or the torus. The sphere is the only surface that has this property of loops: it is simply connected.

Poincaré Conjecture

In 1904, the French mathematician Henri Poincaré conjectured about whether this property of whether or not a loop could be shrunk was true for a particular mathematical object called a 3-sphere. (A 3-sphere is not simply a solid ball; it exists in four-dimensional space but can be thought of as a solid ball whose entire surface is just one point!) What Poincaré thought was going to be a relatively simple generalization from a surface to a 3-sphere turned out to be intractable. So famous did the unproved Poincaré conjecture become that a prize of $1 million was offered for a proof as one of the "Clay Millennium Prizes." Grigori Perelman (see p. 160) published a proof on the internet in 2002/3, but has yet to claim the prize.

• A loop on a sphere can be shrunk to a point.

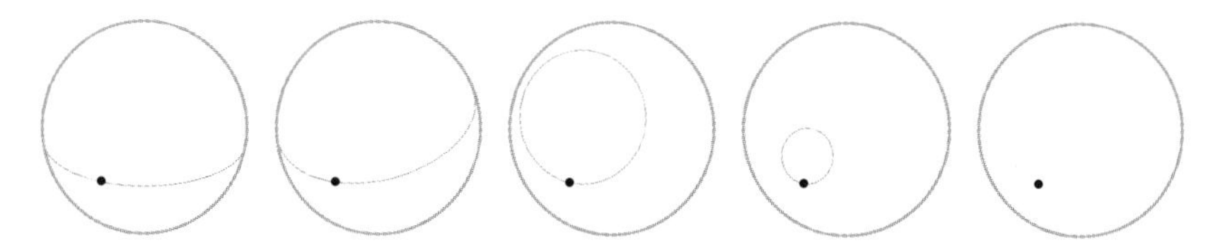

Profile

Jules Henri Poincaré

Poincaré could be considered one of the great geniuses of all time. He contributed to different areas of pure and applied mathematics: celestial mechanics, fluid mechanics, optics, electricity, telegraphy, capillarity, elasticity, thermodynamics, potential theory, quantum theory, theory of relativity, and physical cosmology. In mathematics he contributed in particular to work on topology with what we now call Poincaré's conjecture.

The Life of Poincaré

Jules Henri Poincaré was born in 1854 in Nancy, France, to an influential and well-educated family. His father was Professor of Medicine at the University of Nancy and his cousin became President of France. He had diphtheria as a child and he was taught at home by his mother before going to school—a school now called the Lycée Henri Poincaré in his honor. He excelled at all subjects, and was declared "a monster of mathematics." He went on to study mining engineering, physics, and mathematics in Paris. After his doctorate he taught first at the University of Caen, then, in 1886 he was nominated for the chair of mathematical physics and probability at the Sorbonne in Paris. The following year, at 32, he was elected to the French Academy of Sciences. In 1909 he was elected to the prestigious Académie Française. He taught at the Sorbonne until his death, following an operation, in 1912, when he was 58. He was married and had four children.

The Mind of a Genius

Poincaré wrote about his thought processes, and described them to his colleague Toulouse, who recorded the conversations in a book about Poincaré.

Poincaré had an astonishing memory, and he remembered the line and the page of particular texts he had read, and he also remembered verbatim by ear. He kept very precise working hours, doing mathematical research for just four hours a day, from 10 till noon, and from 5 until 7 pm. He started always from basic principles rather than

A PUBLIC PIONEER

Poincaré worked on what is called the three-body problem, which involves calculating the gravitational interaction of three orbiting bodies in the solar system. In the course of studying this problem, Poincaré discovered chaos theory. In 1887, Oscar II, King of Sweden, offered a prize for a solution to the problem. Poincaré was awarded the prize.

He initiated a French national project to decimalize time and longitude, but other countries were not enthusiastic about taking it up, so it was dropped. However, he was instrumental in synchronizing clocks worldwide and setting up international time zones.

Einstein's first paper on relativity in 1905 was published three months after Poincaré had published a paper on the same subject. Einstein later said that Poincaré had been a pioneer of the work on relativity.

Poincaré developed ideas in the field of topology, in particular the topology of a sphere. The Poincaré conjecture is a theorem about the characterization of the three-dimensional sphere (see p. 157).

Poincaré published books and articles to popularize mathematics and science for the layperson, and created a public interest in science.

building on previous thinking, working with such intense concentration he was hard to distract. He then stopped and expected his subconscious mind to continue the work, "like a bee flying from flower to flower." He always solved ideas in his head first before writing them down. He did not work on new ideas in the evening so that his sleep would not be disturbed, but read articles in journals instead. He wrote that a mathematician "experiences in his work the same impression as an artist; his pleasure is as great and of the same nature." He believed that logic was essential to an understanding of mathematics, but that intuition was necessary for the invention of new ideas. At his funeral he was described as "a poet of the infinite, a bard of science."

"What is it indeed that gives us the feeling of elegance in a solution, in a demonstration? It is the harmony of the diverse parts, their symmetry, their happy balance; in a word it is all that introduces order, all that gives unity, that permits us to see clearly and to comprehend at once both the ensemble and the details."—***Henri Poincaré***

Loops

THE PROBLEM:

Harry saw a magician do a trick with a belt. The magician rolled the belt into a spiral coil that looked like this.

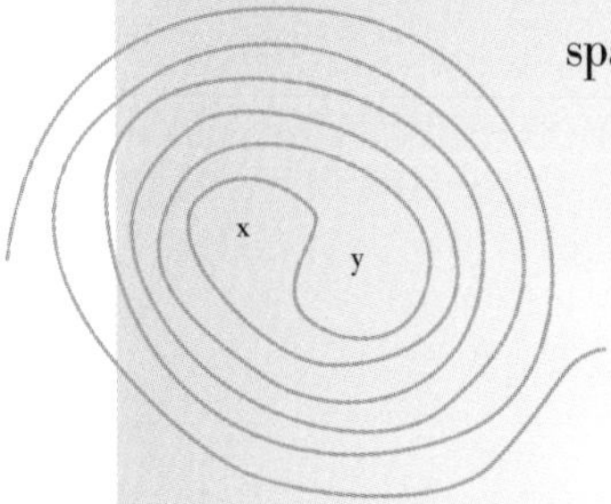

She asked Harry to put a finger in either of the spaces *x* or *y*. The magician picked up the ends of the belt and pulled and Harry's finger was trapped in a loop.

The magician repeated this several times: sometimes Harry's finger was caught in a loop and sometimes it was not. The magician then performed the trick that was to predict whether or not Harry's finger would be trapped or set free. Before Harry put his finger in the spiral she would predict "free" or "trapped." Every time she was correct. Harry wants to know if the magician has psychic powers, is just very lucky, or is pulling a con trick.

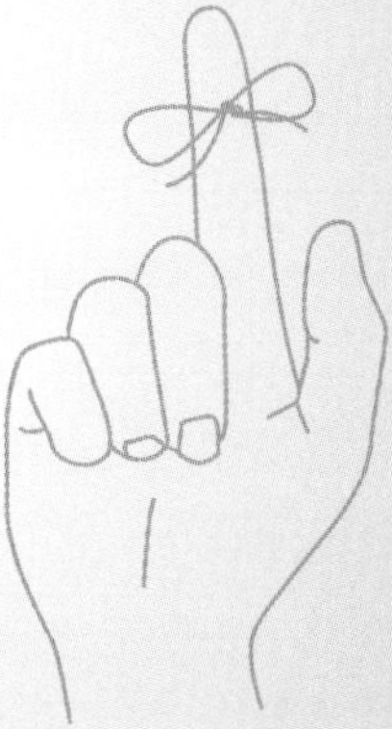

THE METHOD:

This is purely a trick and based on a simple piece of topology. You can do it with a length of thick string or a long belt. You fold the string in half then wind it into a spiral, creating two identical loops in the center—one the loop created by folding the string, and the other created by the first turn of the coil. The important thing is to make these loops look identical. The challenge, as for Harry, is to decide which of these loops will hold "fast" if you put your finger (or the blunt end of a pencil) in it and which will allow the magician to pull the loop away free.

Although one of the loops on the table was the original one created by folding the string, it does not matter which you put your finger in—the magician has complete control over whether or not your finger will be trapped.

The magician picks up end X first and uncoils it clockwise to meet and pick up end Y. She continues to unwind the ends together, clockwise, until they come all the way round to the right. Pulling them away to the right makes a loop that holds fast (the original loop formed by folding the string).

On the other hand, picking up Y first and moving that round clockwise to then pick up X has the effect of turning the loop inside out. It is now the other loop that holds fast.

THE SOLUTION:

Harry was the victim of an old scam known as "fast and loose." Some think the phrase was coined by Shakespeare, as he alludes to the scam in *Antony and Cleopatra*, but the scam is earlier than that and the phrase appears to pre-date the play, although our common use of it to mean "reckless or thoughtless" is the result of Shakespeare's use. A variety of the scam using a closed loop was called "On the Barrelhead" as it was often played on barrel tops on the docks tricking sailors out of their wages. Harry would be better off taking up a magic career getting tied up in chains.

• Whether you select *x* or *y*, you are bound to lose.

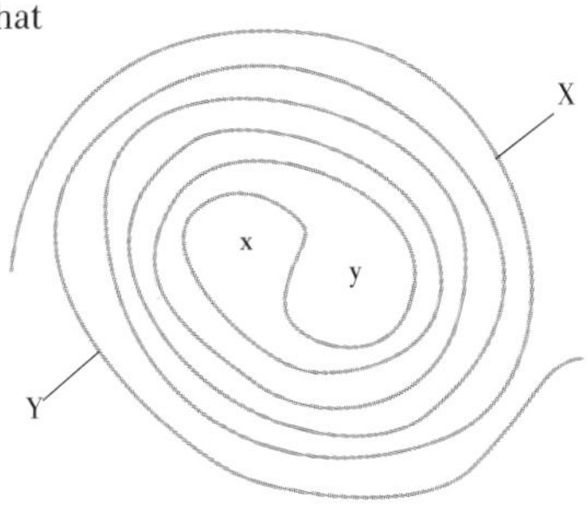

Profile # Grigori Perelman

Grigori Perelman, sometimes known as Grisha Perelman, is a Russian mathematician, born in 1966, who has made significant contributions to Riemannian geometry, and in solving the Poincaré conjecture, posed in 1904 (see p. 157). This is one of the most important and difficult open problems in mathematics.

The Life of Perelman

Perelman was born in Leningrad to a Jewish family. His father was an electrical engineer who liked to give Perelman brain teasers to solve and taught him chess, and his mother was a mathematics teacher. He had a younger sister who also became a mathematician. At 14 he was top of the Leningrad mathematics club and attended the Leningrad Mathematical Center for Gifted Students. In 1982 he won a gold medal at the International Mathematical Olympiad with a perfect score. He went on to the Leningrad State University and gained a PhD with a dissertation on Euclidean geometry. He then went on to work at the Steklov Institute of Mathematics in Leningrad.

After the collapse of the Soviet Union, he was invited to the USA, and he went for a year in 1992 to the New York State University. Perelman enjoyed the freedom of the United States, where he was able to become something of an eccentric. He grew his nails and hair long—a fellow mathematician said "he looked like Rasputin." He went on to the University of California at Berkeley to work on the Poincaré conjecture. He subsequently turned down many offers of positions in American universities and returned to St. Petersburg as a researcher at the Steklov Institute. He lived with his mother and became more and more reclusive. From 2006 it is thought that he gave up mathematical work altogether.

The Solution to the Poincaré Conjecture

In 2002, Perelman posted an article on the Internet, on a website called arXiv.org, a site for articles that are ready to be published in mathematical journals. He followed this with two other postings, together presenting a solution to the Poincaré conjecture. Perelman did not go on to present his solution in a formal refereed paper, and seemed uninterested in any honors that his discovery might bring. In 2006 the International Mathematical Union awarded Perelman the prestigious Fields Medal for his work on the Poincaré conjecture, but he refused to accept the medal and would not attend the conference. He said, "It is irrelevant to me. Everyone understood that if the proof is correct no other recognition is needed."

• Grigori Perelman, photographed sometime before he resigned from his position at the Steklov Institute.

Luitzen Brouwer

Luitzen Egbertus Jan Brouwer (1881–1966) was known to his friends as Bertus, and in the mathematics world as L. E. J. Brouwer (pronounced BROWver). He was a Dutch mathematician and philosopher who worked on topology, set theory, measure theory, and complex analysis. In his early work he focused on the topology of Euclidean space.

At school Brouwer was an outstanding student and finished his studies at the age of 14. He also excelled at university and mainly studied on his own rather than attending lectures. His doctoral thesis contributed to the ideas of Poincaré and Russell on the nature of mathematics. Brouwer invented the term "intuitionism," by which he maintained that the foundations of mathematics lie in the individual mathematician's intuition, thereby making mathematics into an intrinsically subjective activity. In the classical, logical approach to mathematics, a statement is either true or false. Intuitionism requires proof for a statement to be true or false, and allows that some statements are not provable—that is, mathematics is not a complete logical system waiting to be discovered and proved in its entirety, but is a construction of the mind. These ideas were considered controversial at the time, and were disapproved of by his thesis supervisor, Korteweg.

Brouwer lectured at the University of Amsterdam, and eventually took over the Chair of Mathematics from Korteweg. He was treated well by the university—he only appeared at the university once a week, and he would not have his lectures interrupted with questions. He did not lecture on topology, his specialist subject, but only on intuitionism.

In his lifetime he was elected to the Royal Dutch Academy of Sciences, the Royal Society of London, the Berlin Academy of Sciences, and the Göttingen Academy of Sciences. He was made Knight in the Order of the Dutch Lion in 1932.

The Hairy Ball Theorem

The hairy ball theorem states that if you have a ball completely covered with hairs, it is impossible to comb the hairs down so that they all lie flat. Some hair must be sticking straight up. It's also called "the cow's-lick problem." Brouwer proved the theorem in 1912. This is how he stated the theorem: "Given a tangential vector field on the surface of a sphere in three-dimensional space, there must be at least one point where the field is zero."

A donut does not present the same problem. If you have a torus covered in hairs, you can comb the hairs down so that they all lie flat.

The hairy ball theorem has applications to wind patterns around Earth: given that there is wind at all times somewhere on the earth, there must also always be a cyclone somewhere (that is, where there is no wind, in the eye of the cyclone). The theorem has applications, too, to computer graphics.

"Mathematics is nothing more, nothing less, than the exact part of our thinking."—*Luitzen Brouwer*

FRACTALS

Mathematicians have often spoken of the beauty of mathematics, a beauty arising from the elegance of mathematical proof and the way that seemingly disparate branches of mathematics have often come together after a new insight. More recently, the beauty of mathematics has become more apparent to others through computer-generated fractals.

Koch Snowflake

Take an equilateral triangle. Divide each side into thirds and construct another, smaller, equilateral triangle in the middle third of each side. A six-pointed star is created with 12 edges.

Repeat this process of thirding and constructing a triangle on the 12 edges and continue on each of the resulting edges, resulting in a snowflake with increasingly wrinkly edges.

First appearing in 1904 in a paper by Swedish mathematician Helge von Koch, the Koch snowflake has, not surprisingly, finite area. Calculating the area is not easy, but you can draw a circle around the design that places an upper bound on the value of the area. The perimeter of the shape is curious: it is infinitely long and can never be measured. This is a result of the construction of the crinkly perimeter. As you measure this with increasing accuracy, by zooming in, so the perimeter continues to twist and turn, making a definitive final measurement impossible.

Crinkly Coastlines

The Koch snowflake remained a mathematical curiosity until Benoît Mandelbrot took an interest in a paper written by the relatively obscure mathematician, Lewis Richardson. In 1961, Richardson published a paper called "How long is the coastline of Britain?" Far from being a trivial measurement question, Richardson applied similar logic to measuring the coastline as that applied to the perimeter of the Koch snowflake: the more you zoom in to the coastline to measure it more accurately, the longer the coastline becomes. Imagine, for example, finding the coastline of Britain from a satellite image and comparing this with an estimate obtained by driving around the coastal roads. The latter will be more accurate and longer than the former. Walking the coastline allows for more nooks and crannies than the roads: more accurate and longer again. And an ant walking the coastline? Smaller units, more accuracy but increasing length. Unlike the Koch snowflake, the physics of the world means that the coastline must stop getting longer at some point, but the drift of the argument is similar.

No Smoothness

Constructing the Koch snowflake involves a simple repeating rule, an iteration or recursion. One result of this is that whatever scale the snowflake is examined at, it is always detailed, in the sense that there is no scale at which the perimeter is smooth. Mandelbrot was interested in the fact that this is a property of many things in the real world: fern leaves, broccoli heads, blood vessels. As you zoom in to examine these objects, there is a sense of infinite detail and infinite length. Most importantly, there is an absence of the smoothness that is the bedrock of Euclidean geometry. Mandelbrot coined the term "fractal" to describe shapes with this property of being "detailed" whatever the scale.

Iteration

The Mandelbrot set (or M-set as it is familiarly known) is one of, if not the most, iconic fractals.

Like the Koch snowflake, the M-set is created by a simple recursive, iterative rule. Mandelbrot was examining the simple formula $xn + 1 = xn2 + c$. What this simply means is taking a starting value for x and a constant value c, you calculate the next value by squaring x and adding c. This new value is "plugged" into the equation and the process repeated, in theory, for infinity. For example, with $xo = 0$ and $c = 1$, the first few terms of the iteration are 0, 1, 2, 5, 26, 677, 458,330 . . . As you might expect, the values here continue to get increasingly large: the series diverges to infinity.

Mandelbrot's amazing discovery was that using complex number values for x and c (numbers involving the square root of -1) and an initial starting value for x of 0, changing the value of c could produce two different results. Like the example above, many values of c result in series that diverge to infinity. But there are an infinite number of values that do not: this set of values is the M-set.

Simple Chaos

Fractals are often described as being the mathematics of chaos, but they are actually very simple, being based on recursive rules, and, while unpredictable, are far from chaotic.

Pop-Up

THE PROBLEM:

Georgia saw some lovely "pop-up" greetings cards at a craft fair and would like to make some herself. As she is interested in mathematics, she would like her cards to have a mathematical flavor.

THE METHOD:

There is a simple technique for creating a pop-up card that produces a fractal. The beauty of the product belies the simplicity of its construction, in much the same way that fractals in the real world produce complex and stunning objects from simple rules.

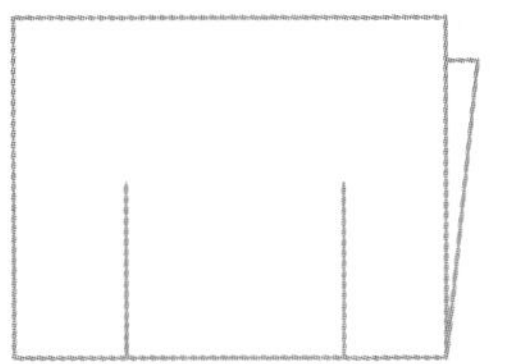

Start by taking a piece of paper and folding it in half.

Make two cuts, each up from the folded edge. Each cut should be about one-quarter of the way in from the edge of the paper and go halfway up from the fold to the top. It's not necessary to measure this out accurately: judging it by eye will suffice.

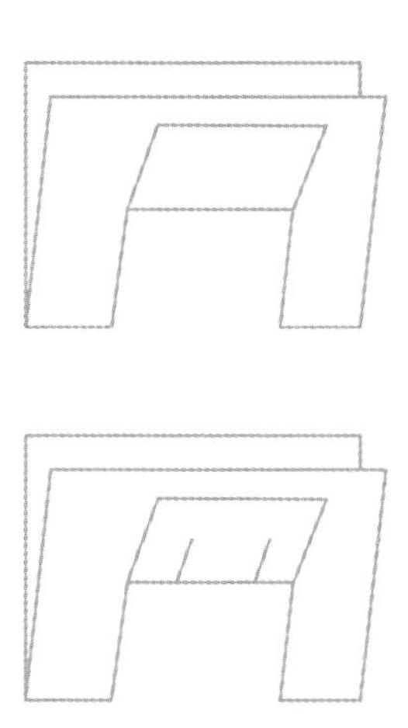

Glue this inside another piece of paper or card of the same size and folded to create the card. Opening the card at right angles should reveal a series of open-ended cuboids, stacked upon each other, and getting smaller with each iteration.

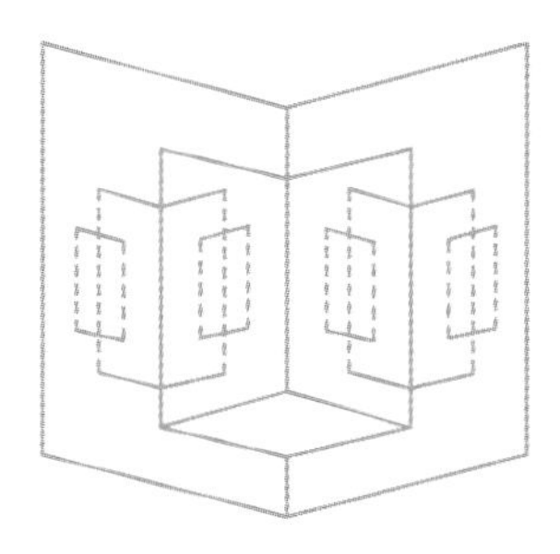

Treat the new fold created as a reduced-size version of the first fold: two cuts each a quarter from the corners and going halfway to the top.

Fold and repeat. Keep doing this as many times as you can. It will depend on the size and thickness of the paper, but you should be able to do this four or five times.

Now carefully unfold everything. The fractal is created by reversing the folds so that rather than being folded on the outside of the original fold, they are tucked inside. You are aiming to create a series of "steps" that get progressively smaller and are nested on top of each other. It helps to keep folding everything flat along the first fold line, but now with the steps inside.

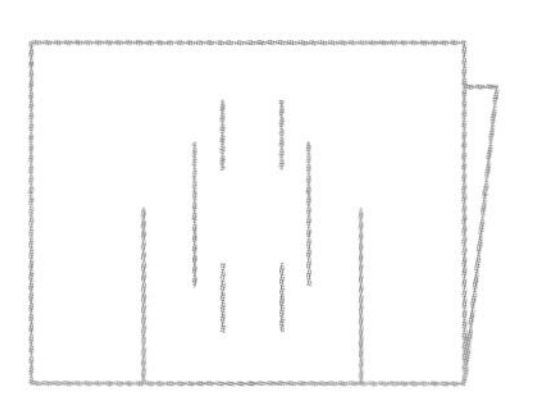

THE SOLUTION:

The simple rule of cutting and folding and repeating but getting proportionally smaller does create a fractal. The card has the main property of fractals in being self-similar: each part of the pop-up mirrors the whole. The mathematically curious Georgia should be able to find a number of interesting relationships in the elements of the fractal.

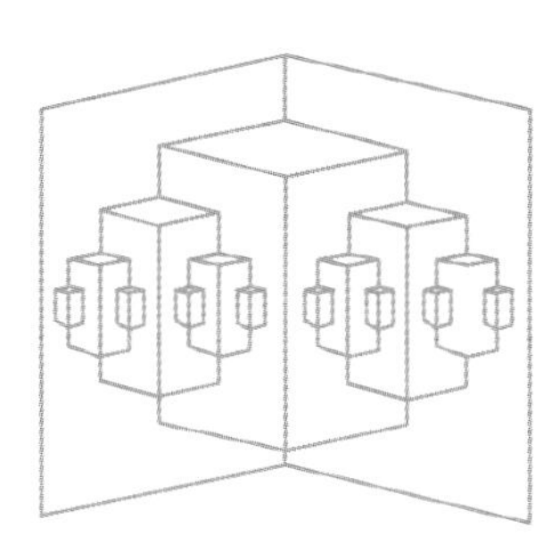

Exercise 29

The Chaos Game

THE PROBLEM:

Michael was playing around with using a die to randomly generate a pattern. He started by marking the corners of an equilateral triangle and randomly marking a fourth point within the triangle.

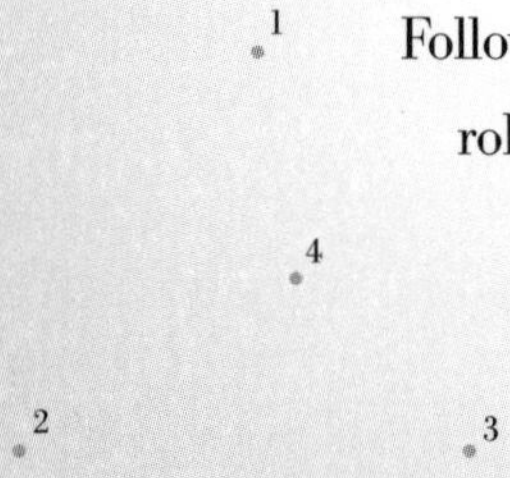

1

4

2 3

Following simple roles determined by the roll of the die, Michael marked in more dots. Does he produce just a random scattering of dots within the triangle?

THE METHOD:

The rules to follow here are simple. Having set up the initial three points, roll a die.

Dot 4 is the starting point. If the score on the die is 1 or 2, the next dot (5) is marked as the halfway point between 4 and 1.

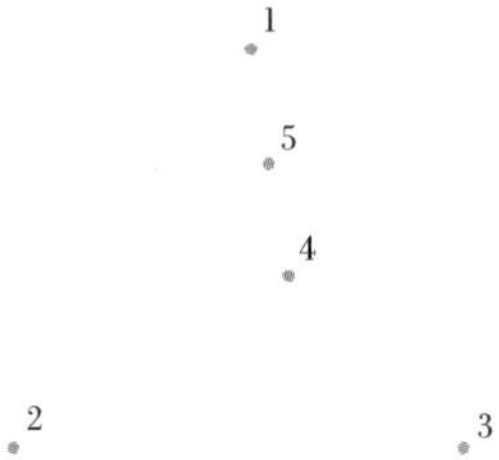

1

5

4

2 3

If, however, the score on the die is 3 or 4, then dot 5 is marked halfway between 4 and 2. A score of 5 or 6 produces dot 5 as halfway between 4 and 3.

Dot 5 then becomes the starting point and the process of rolling the die and repeating marking the halfway point between 5 and 1, 2 or 3 depending on the score, to create dot 6. And so on.

Far from creating a random collection of points within the triangle, a pattern begins to emerge.

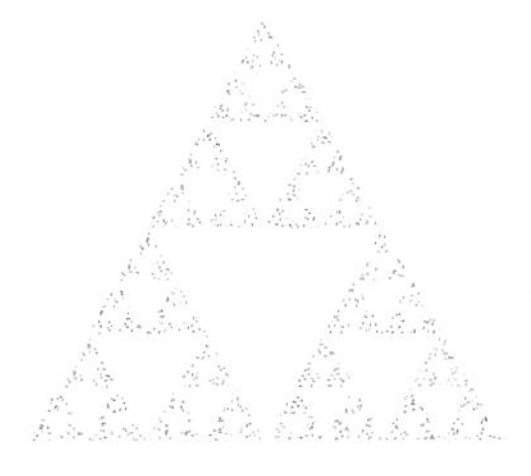

As you continue, a distinct and familiar fractal emerges: the Sierpinski triangle.

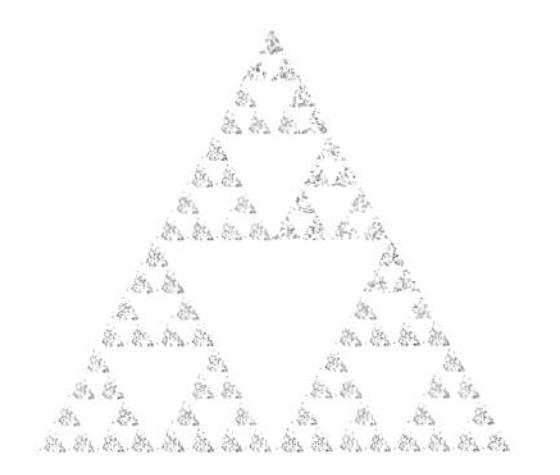

SIERPINSKI'S TRIANGLE

Wacław Sierpinski (1882–1969) was a Polish mathematician who made an outstanding contribution to set theory. In 1915 he described what Mandelbrot later called a fractal in the form we now know as Sierpinski's triangle. This is a simple form of fractal, and easily constructed. It is recursive and so contains an infinite number of triangles. It starts as an equilateral triangle, then at each iteration new triangles are formed at the midpoint of the original triangle or triangles.

THE SOLUTION:

This game, invented in the 1980s by Michael Barnsley, demonstrates how random and unpredictable events—the scores on rolling a die—can lead to regularity in the form of a fractal. Different starting points can generate different fractals, for example, fern-like fronds. The fractal nature of the world is based on simple iterative rules.

Profile # Benoît Mandelbrot

Mandelbrot was responsible for the current interest in fractals. He demonstrated how fractals occur in mathematics and in the natural world—the Mandelbrot set of fractals is named after him. Mandelbrot's work on fractals has contributed to chaos theory and to many applications in science and mathematics.

The Life of Mandelbrot

Benoît Mandelbrot was born in Warsaw in 1924 to a Jewish family from Lithuania. In 1936, when he was 11, the family fled from Poland to France. His family was intellectual—his mother was a doctor, his father was a scholar who supported the family as a clothing manufacturer, and Mandelbrot was taught mathematics by two of his uncles. Although he went to good schools, his education was fractured by the Second World War and German occupation, and the need for survival and the fear for his life. He later attributed his ability for lateral thinking to this unconventional education, and to the time he had on his own to think and develop ideas. He claimed he had never learned the alphabet nor progressed beyond the five-times table.

He resumed his studies in Paris and in 1945 attended the École Polytechnique. From 1947 to 49 he studied aeronautics at the California Institute of Technology, then returned to Paris to obtain a PhD in mathematical sciences. From 1949 to 1958, Mandelbrot was a staff member of the Centre National de la Recherche Scientifique in Paris. In 1955 he married and moved to Geneva in Switzerland. In 1958 he and his wife moved to the USA, where Mandelbrot joined the IBM Thomas J. Watson Research Center in New York. In an environment that encouraged his explorations, Mandelbrot remained there for 32 years, becoming an IBM Fellow. During this time he was also made visiting professor of mathematics and economics at Harvard University. On his retirement from IBM he became Sterling Professor of Mathematical Sciences at Yale University. He has been awarded many prizes, including the Legion of Honor in France. An asteroid, the 27500 Mandelbrot, was named after him.

Key Works

Mandelbrot studied a range of topics that seemed unrelated: noise in telephone lines, fluctuations in the cotton commodity markets and linguistics. He came to see that all of these had mathematics in common: fractals. He also looked at the problem of measuring coastlines—and proposed that their length depended on how you measure them. Go out

• A computer-generated fractal image presents infinite detail in a beautiful way.

into space, and they become a line or even a dot. But zoom in, and the closer you are to the detail of the coastline, the more indentations you see, even down to the raggedness of the rocks, and the holes within the rocks. Mandelbrot coined the work "fractals" to describe the zooming-in to natural irregularities. He wrote about his discovery: "Clouds are not spheres, mountains are not cones, coastlines are not circles, and bark is not smooth, nor does lightning travel in a straight line." He pursued this investigation of irregularities in nature with the help of computers, which led him to develop the Mandelbrot Set of fractals.

The study of fractals has led scientists to investigate rock porosity, the strength of steel, the growth of lungs, the irregular walking pattern of people with Parkinson's disease, the healthy heartbeat, the size, location, and timing of natural disasters, and so on. Fractals have inspired creativity in art: fractals are found in African art and architecture, in digital art and animation, and fractal techniques are used by composers such as Györgi Ligeti and Arvo Pärt. Fractals are also used in stock market prices.

"A cloud is made of billows upon billows upon billows that look like clouds. As you come closer to a cloud you don't get something smooth, but irregularities at a smaller scale."—***Benoît Mandelbrot***

SPACE-FILLING CURVES

We began (see p. 14) by observing that Euclid regarded points and lines as having no breadth—a drawn line clearly has a width, but a "mathematical line" (existing in the imagination) has zero width. Clearly that means that, no matter how closely packed together we imagine a series of mathematical (as opposed to drawn) lines, they can never fill up a space: the sum of a series of zeros must be zero. Italian mathematician Giuseppe Peano rocked the mathematical world by demonstrating otherwise.

Wriggly Curves

Like fractals, the space-filling curve devised by Peano was based on simple iterative rules of construction. By taking a simple motif and repeatedly making it more and more crinkly, Peano was able to show that, at infinity, the curve would completely fill a square area with no gaps. Obviously, it is impossible to show the curve at infinity, as by that time the square is completely shaded in. But we can see the first few iterations for creating the curve.

• At infinity, the Peano curve completely fills the area.

• First eight steps toward building the Hilbert curve.

Groundbreaker

A year after Peano's discovery, the German mathematician David Hilbert created another. This idea that something that had essentially been thought of as having no thickness—a line—was shocking to the world of mathematics and was described as the mathematical equivalent of an "earthquake" (David Darling) and leaving mathematical meaning in "ruins" (Naum Valentin).

Things got even worse when it was shown that these curves could be extended further and used to fill three dimensions. The positive outcome to all this unsettling was that mathematicians had to rethink what was actually meant by dimensions. It has now become accepted that objects are not confined to being one-, two-, or three-dimensional. Fractional dimensions less than one are possible and objects like the Koch snowflake (see p. 166) are accepted as having dimension of about 1.26. Named after the mathematician Felix Hausdorff, these fractional dimensions are used to measure fractals. The topological dimension of a coastline (treating it as a smooth curve) is one, whereas acknowledging the wrinkliness of coastlines gives them a Hausdorff dimension greater than one but less than two. So, for example, the west coast of Great Britain has a Hausdorff dimension of about 1.25.

Far from being esoteric mathematical ideas, fractional dimensions have applications in biology and geology.

INDEX

TERMS AND SYMBOLS

Congruent two geometrical shapes are congruent if they are the same size and shape (although they may be in different positions).

Conic the curve created when a plane intersects a cone. Depending on the angle of the plane, different conic sections can be created: parabola, ellipse, circle, or hyperbola.

Euclidean geometry the study of plane and solid figures based on the axioms and theorems developed by the Greek mathematician Euclid.

Fibonacci numbers a sequence in which each subsequent number is the sum of the previous two. The first ten numbers in the sequence are 0, 1, 1, 2, 3, 5, 8, 13, 21, and 34.

Fractals from the Latin work for "fragmented," fractals are a complex set of geometrical figures with the property of being "self-similar": any part of a fractal is similar to the whole figure. Real objects such as coastlines or broccoli heads display fractal self-similarity.

Golden ratio a ratio constructed by dividing a line segment into two unequal parts such that the ratio of the larger part to the whole line is the same as the ratio of the smaller part to the larger. Although an older mathematical phenomenon, the golden ratio occurs in the study of fractals.

Great circle created when a plane slicing through a sphere passes through the sphere's center. The shortest path between two points on the surface of a sphere passes along an arc of a great circle.

Plane any flat two-dimensional surface. In Euclidean geometry, referring to the plane means the surface extends infinitely.

Pi (π) the constant value obtained in Euclidean geometry from the ratio of any circle's circumference (the distance around the circle) to its diameter (the distance across through the center of the circle).

Platonic solids polyhedra whose faces are all congruent regular polygons and where the same number of faces meet at each vertex (corner). There are five Platonic solids: tetrahedron, cube (or hexahedron), octahedron, dodecahedron, and icosahedron.

Polygon plane figures bounded by straight-line segments. A regular polygon, for example a square or equilateral triangle, has all sides the same length and equal angles at every vertex.

Polyhedron a three-dimensional shape with flat faces made from polygons.

Topology the study of spatial properties that are preserved when objects are deformed, for example through stretching (hence being popularly known as "rubber-sheet" geometry). A cube is topologically equivalent to a sphere.